LITTLE DID WE KNOW

EYEWITNESSES TO THE ADVENT

KENNETH A. WINTER

WildernessLessons

JOIN MY READERS' GROUP FOR UPDATES AND FUTURE RELEASES

Please join my Readers' Group so i can send you a free book, as well as updates and information about future releases, etc.

See the back of the book for details on how to sign up.

∾

Little Did We Know

... Eyewitnesses to the Advent

The Eyewitnesses Collection - Book 1

Published by:

Kenneth A. Winter

WildernessLessons, LLC

Richmond, Virginia

United States of America

kenwinter.org

wildernesslessons.com

Edited by Sheryl Martin Hash

Cover design by Dennis Waterman

Cover photo by Lightstock

ISBN 978-1-7341930-4-6 (soft cover)

ISBN 978-1-7341930-5-3 (e-book)

ISBN 978-1-7341930-6-0 (large print)

Library of Congress Control Number: 2020907094

DEDICATION

To the men, women and their families
who have responded to God's call
to be witnesses to those who have not yet heard
the name of Jesus,

and

To those who have and will come to know Jesus
through their witness.

~

How then will they call on Him in whom they have not believed? And how are
they to believe in Him of whom they have never heard? And how are they to
hear without someone preaching? And how are they to preach unless they are
sent? As it is written, "How beautiful are the feet of those who preach the good
news!"
Romans 10:14-15 (ESV)

~

CONTENTS

FROM THE AUTHOR

A word of explanation for those of you who are new to my writing.

～

You will notice that whenever i use the pronoun "I" referring to myself, i have chosen to use a lowercase "i." This only applies to me personally (in the Preface). i do not impose my personal conviction on any of the characters in this book. It is not a typographical error. i know this is contrary to proper English grammar and accepted editorial style guides. i drive editors (and "spell check") crazy by doing this. But years ago, the Lord convicted me – personally – that in all things i must decrease and He must increase.

And as a way of continuing personal reminder, from that day forward, i have chosen to use a lowercase "i" whenever referring to myself. Because of the same conviction, i use a capital letter for any pronoun referring to God throughout the entire book. The style guide for the New Living Translation (NLT) does not share that conviction. However, you will see that i have intentionally made that slight revision and capitalized any pronoun referring to God in my quotations of Scripture from the NLT. If i have violated any style guides as a result, please accept my apology, but i must honor this conviction.

Lastly, regarding this matter – this is a <u>personal</u> conviction – and i share it only so you will understand why i have chosen to deviate from normal editorial practice. i am in no way suggesting or endeavoring to have anyone else subscribe to my conviction. Thanks for your understanding.

～

PREFACE

~

This is a fictional work set in the midst of true events centering around the arrival of Jesus, God's only Son. It is a collection of twenty-five individual short stories, each a firsthand account from a prophetic voice of, or an eyewitness to, the birth of Jesus. Each story stands alone but also builds on a previous story. i have chosen to tell these stories through the eyes of multiple "eyewitnesses" because not everyone responded or reacted the same way. Not every witness was joyful about His birth. Not every witness was expectant of His birth. And not every witness was accepting of His birth.

The writers of the Gospels of Matthew and Luke were led by the Holy Spirit to write just what the Heavenly Father wanted us to know about the birth of our Savior. There were many details related to how others reacted to His birth that were left unwritten. Those unwritten details prompt questions that we won't know the answers to until we stand before our Lord. And by then, it may not even matter.

i have taken great care in the writing of this work to guard the sanctity and truth of the Gospel message. My hope is that this book prompts you to consider the truth as recorded in Scripture. My additions are purely for your reading entertainment as you consider those truths.

The majority of the "eyewitnesses" come directly from the pages of Scripture. You will easily recognize their names. However, where the Bible is silent, i have chosen to add background details about many of these people that are either purely fictional or conjectures not confirmed in Scripture. These background details are added to further the telling of the stories. There is a listing of characters at the back of this book to assist you in knowing where i have added fictional details.

Some of the "eyewitnesses" are seen in Scripture – but not necessarily tied to the advent. Their inclusion in this work is either the result of reasonable conjecture or complete fiction. But i have included them because of the unique perspective they bring.

Lastly, a number of the "eyewitnesses" are complete fiction. For example, i do not believe that Joseph attempted to find a room in Bethlehem at the first century "Holiday Inn." i believe he intended to lodge with family. So, a few of the fictional characters are family members i have created to receive Joseph and Mary. You will not find them in Scripture!

Similar to my novels, you will also encounter fictional twists and turns that are an attempt to fill in the blanks where Scripture is silent regarding certain day-to-day events. Again, my prayer is that nothing in the story detracts from scriptural truth, but rather, while remaining true to the biblical story, tells it in a way that creates an interesting and enjoyable reading experience.

Throughout the stories, many instances of dialogue are direct quotes from Scripture. Whenever i am quoting Scripture, it has been italicized. The Scripture references are included in the back of this book. Those remaining instances of dialogue not italicized are a part of the fictional stories in order to help advance the storyline. However, i have endeavored to use Scripture as the basis in forming any added dialogue spoken by historical characters, with the intent that i do not do anything that detracts from the overall message of God's Word.

Since the advent of Jesus is the Father's fulfillment of His promise, we start with His promise. We will quickly look at how that promise carried forward within His chosen people from one generation to the next.

Little did they know how God's promise would unfold. Little did they know exactly when the Father would send His Son. In like manner, little do we know exactly when Jesus will return. But like those eyewitnesses of the first century, we have already been given the promise. His coming is foretold. If His return occurs in our lifetime, i pray we will be eyewitnesses who are ready and watching to receive Him.

As i was writing these stories, i was encouraged to also write a set of stories for children. That suggestion blossomed into a companion book to go along with this one. **Not Too Little To Know** is an illustrated "chapter" book designed for children ages 8 and up. It contains ten short stories that are first-person accounts of a child or young teen who also was an eyewitness to the events surrounding the advent of Jesus.

Several of the children are fictional characters, but there is an explanation at the end of each story describing what is fiction and what is fact. Each of the ten children is introduced in this book. So, you will see how the first-person accounts of the two books complement one another.

For example, we start with Isaac's account of the day he and his father experienced the reality that God would provide His own Lamb to be sacrificed. Then we turn to nine other children who were contemporaries of Jesus, including Salome (a neighbor girl who encouraged Mary), Yanzu (a servant boy who traveled with the wise men), and Khati (a young boy who lent a helping hand to Joseph and Mary when they arrived in Egypt).

Not Too Little To Know stands alone as a chronicle of the advent for children, but it can also be used in conjunction with this book to help further family conversations about the advent. More information about this children's version is available at the end of this book.

As with my novels, i pray that this book stimulates conversation. So, i have established a Facebook discussion group for that purpose. If you are on Facebook, i invite you to join the **Little Did We Know** group and i look forward to hearing from you there.

May the grace of the Lord Jesus Christ be with you as you celebrate the advent of our Savior.

∾

LUKE – THE PHYSICIAN

My name is Luke and I'm a physician by training. Unlike most everyone else you will hear from in these written accounts, I am not a Jew. I am a Greek Gentile. I am the son of an affluent physician and his wife who settled in the city of Antioch in Syria. If you were to ask me, I would tell you that Antioch is my home. That is where I was born and raised, and that is where I practiced the art of medicine for twenty years. However, for most of the past forty years, I have rarely been there. I have been traveling throughout Asia and Europe to some of the most extraordinary places.

I never aspired to be well-known. I am not a gifted orator, nor do I seek to be the center of attention. I have always desired to serve others, meet their needs, and live my life in prosperous comfort and peace. I would describe myself as a dedicated student of life – not an influential leader. But one day my life path changed, and I said farewell to the comforts of a prosperous medical practice. Instead, I have traveled on a mission with much greater purpose.

I have slept in palaces and in prisons. I have traveled with friends under the watchful guard of Roman soldiers. I have experienced storms at sea and even a shipwreck or two. I have seen my friends stoned by crowds that adored them one minute and despised them the next. I, too, have been welcomed into towns from which I was later forcibly removed. My journey has taken many unexpected turns as I have become an eyewitness to some of the most extraordinary events in history.

I received my medical training from some of the finest physicians practicing throughout what was once called the Greek empire. The Romans dominated the Greek empire centuries ago, but my family has always considered itself to be Greek. Though Antioch became part of the Roman empire over sixty years before I was born, I have never considered myself to be a Roman.

But under Roman rule, our city became the third largest city in the empire with a population of over five hundred thousand people – coming from a multiplicity of cultures and languages. Though I consider myself to be a Greek, I will confess that through my travels I have come to appreciate the freedoms that the official stamp of my Roman citizenship affords me.

Growing up, my religious beliefs centered around the gods of our Greek ancestors. But over the years, the continuing influx of other cultures into Antioch brought a myriad of religious beliefs, including those with doctrines of salvation, of death and regeneration, and of promises of an afterlife. Those beliefs began to intrigue me. My scientific mind began to question the legitimacy of the cultic practices of our beliefs in Zeus, Apollo, and the rest of the Pantheon.

When I was thirty-eight I visited the Cilician city of Tarsus. I encountered a man named Saul who seemed somewhat strange. He was short-statured, very animated when he spoke, and most obviously a Jew. But his beliefs were not like those of the other Jews I had encountered in Antioch. He spoke of a Man by the name of Jesus. But he said that Jesus wasn't like other men – rather, He was the Son of the Almighty God.

. . .

Growing up I had heard all about Hercules, the son of Zeus. So initially, Saul's rantings about this Man claiming to be the Son of God didn't impress me. I knew all about the self-centered, demanding, egotistical deities who had come to earth. But when Saul told me that he had encountered this Jesus personally while traveling to Damascus to persecute His followers, I decided to listen to him.

As impressive as this man's personal experiences were, I became even more intrigued by his stories of this Man named Jesus. This Son of God had spoken of a God who loved me. He had been sent by His Father to walk and live in this world – not to oppress us like the gods I knew – but to set us free! His mission had ultimately led to His death – not for His actions, but for mine!

He had come to save His chosen people – but most had rejected Him. He had even willingly laid down His life so they might have life – without end. And this Jesus had not remained in the grave, He had risen! He was not giving the gift of life without end to His chosen people only. He had extended that gift to all people. Thus, the news of His gift was being carried throughout the land.

These Christ-followers didn't worship a myth or a god made of stone – they worshipped a living Savior. And they were willing to be imprisoned or die for their belief! I had never known anyone willing to die for Zeus! These followers were compelled to tell everyone about Jesus. I had never witnessed such conviction in anyone else!

This risen Savior had called out to Saul in the middle of the road to Damascus. He had temporarily blinded him – not to punish him, but to free him. And then He had miraculously returned Saul's sight. Saul told me how this same risen Savior had led him on a three-year journey through the wilderness of Arabia – teaching him how to be His disciple and preparing him to disciple others. Before that day was over, Saul had convinced me of the truth of this risen Savior. I, too, became a follower of Jesus that day – and I have never looked back!

. . .

When I returned to Antioch, I found others in my city who also had recently become followers of Jesus. In a few short months, God brought my friend Saul and his friend Barnabas to our city to disciple us in our newfound faith. A church was born. We came to be known as Christians – and within a few short years we were sending out messengers from our midst to tell the rest of the world about Jesus. That is how my travels began – and why I gave up my medical practice. But those stories are for another time!

As I spent more time with Saul – who came to be known as Paul – and listened to him tell the story of Jesus to others, I realized there were many who were struggling to believe the accuracy of the stories. One in particular was you, my good friend Theophilus. You and I grew up together long before you became the governor of our city.

One night as you and I were speaking about Jesus you said to me, "Luke, I need to know the certainty of the truth of which you speak. Those things which you believe to be true, you heard from this man Paul. What he knows, he attributes to One who spoke to him from heaven. But if what you say is true, this Jesus walked the hills of Galilee and the streets of Jerusalem only twenty short years ago. He was born and crucified all within the past fifty years.

"Surely there are people who have witnessed His birth, His ministry, His death, and His resurrection firsthand. Someone needs to interview those eyewitnesses and capture their stories. Luke, with your scientific mind and your ability as a truth-seeker, you are just the person to gather those accounts!"

It was your words, Theophilus, that continued to echo in my mind. I shared your comments with Paul, and he agreed that I needed to write an account. He then invited me to travel with him. He would introduce me to some of the first disciples of Jesus. From there, I could interview others and begin to assemble a firsthand eyewitness account – not only about the life, death, and resurrection of Jesus, but also about what has happened since He ascended into heaven.

. . .

In the years that followed, I have done just that! By the time I was sixty-three, I had written what is now referred to as the Gospel of Luke. A few years later, I followed the first account with another entitled the Acts of the Apostles – two years before my dear friend and mentor Paul was executed by Emperor Nero. As promised, I sent both of those accounts to you, my friend Theophilus.

In my endeavor to construct a credible account of the facts, I spoke to dozens – perhaps hundreds – of eyewitnesses. I compiled more testimonies than I was able to rightly include in my two accounts. The work became so voluminous that it would be difficult to communicate in its entirety. A library would never contain the number of books that would be needed to tell all of the events pertaining to Jesus, His teachings, and His works.

For example, I was limited as to what I could include regarding the miraculous details of the advent of Jesus as a baby – because those accounts themselves would fill volumes. I had dozens of interviews about that event alone. So, I have decided to organize some of those interviews into this volume with that singular purpose.

As you will see, Theophilus, the first few accounts in this volume are from people who are already deceased – a few for a very long time. But their accounts are critical to this story. They are the messengers of the many prophecies and teachings that were fulfilled through the birth of Jesus.

Since many reading this account will not be familiar with the tenets of Judaism, they will not know the details that Jewish readers would take for granted. It is important that readers know those prophecies and teachings. It is also beneficial for them to understand the requirements under the Jewish laws related to circumcision, religious festivals, offerings, and the like.

. . .

Gratefully, the words of those earlier messengers are not merely "hearsay." Their words have been recorded by trusted authors – including themselves. So, I believe you will concur that they are reliable witnesses. I am presenting them to you here in their first-person form so that I do not add anything to, or take anything away from, their words.

As I approach my eighty-fourth birthday, I am doubtful that I have many days remaining in this life – and that is probably no less true of you, my friend. But my prayer is that you will read these words with an open mind, seeking the One of whom I write. For you see, Jesus did not remain a baby in the manger – rather, He always was the Word of God incarnate, sent to earth to ultimately pay the price for our sin, to achieve victory over death, and to be the one and only Way through which we can have life without end.

One truth that has been universal among all of the eyewitnesses – me included – is that little do any of us fully comprehend where our journey with Him will lead. We don't know the twists or turns in the path ahead. We don't know how He will use the encounters in the journey to bring each of us to a greater understanding of Who He is.

Little did I know where my journey would lead. And little do I know where these accounts will lead you in your journey with the baby in the manger ...

~

ABRAHAM – THE PATRIARCH

I'm a shepherd by the name of Abraham. My father, Terah, named me Abram, then God renamed me Abraham – but I'll tell you more about that later. I was born approximately three hundred years after the great flood. Jehovah God saw that the wickedness of man was great upon the earth; corruption and violence were everywhere. So, God determined to destroy all mankind, save one man and his family. Through them, God would repopulate the earth. That man was Noah – whom God saved because He found him blameless.[1]

But the sin nature that had become a part of Adam and Eve when they disobeyed God continued to live on through Noah. From that one man, the earth is now again filled with people of many clans, languages, and nations. Sadly, most have turned their hearts away from Jehovah God and the land has again become corrupt.

But God made a covenant that He would never again destroy the earth with a flood.[2] Instead, God had a plan to redeem His creation. Because He had always known what was in man's heart, God always had His plan of redemption.

. . .

By the grace of Jehovah God that plan included me. I, too, am a descendant of Noah through his eldest son, Shem. So that seed of Adam courses through my veins, as well. I seek to walk uprightly before God – but I fail. Still, by His grace and not my merit, He chose to bless me and use me as His servant.

I was born in the city of Ur of the Chaldeans, located in southern Mesopotamia on the southwestern shore of the Euphrates River. We were herdsmen and God graciously and bountifully multiplied our herds in that fertile plain. When I was about fifty years old, my father led me and my wife, Sarai (who is also my half-sister), together with our nephew Lot, to drive our herds northward about six hundred miles along the Euphrates River to the city of Haran.

My father saw an opportunity to expand our family enterprise. Haran was a merchant outpost of the Assyrian Empire, situated along a trade route between the Mediterranean Sea and the plains of the middle Tigris. It was a strategic waypoint for trade between Damascus, Babylon, and Nineveh. God further blessed our family and multiplied our wealth over the next twenty-five years.

But my one regret was that Jehovah had not blessed my wife and me with children. We longed for a son, but God in His infinite wisdom chose not to grace us with a child. And now at our advanced ages, it seemed highly unlikely that would ever occur.

Then one day God told me, *"Go from your country and your kindred and your father's house to the land that I will show you. And I will make of you a great nation, and I will bless you and make your name great, so that you will be a blessing. I will bless those who bless you, and him who dishonors you I will curse, and in you all the families of the earth shall be blessed."*[3]

God promised He would make of me a great nation – and yet my wife was barren! But I believed what God said. So, Lot and I each took the portion of our family's possessions that was due us and departed with my father's blessing.

We traveled south along the Mediterranean Sea into the land of Canaan. I did not know where God was leading us, but I knew He *was* leading. We traveled by faith knowing that He would continue to show us each step of the journey.

After stopping over in Damascus to visit with several of our trading partners, we continued south to Shechem. It was there that God again spoke to me saying, *"To your offspring I will give this land."*[4]

Again, God was promising me offspring, and now He was telling me that my offspring would inhabit the very land I was traversing. It was all so much more than I could comprehend, but I knew that nothing was impossible with God!

We stopped in the hill country between Bethel and Ai. There I built an altar to the Lord and called upon Him in praise and worship. There was no question that I would follow Him. After several days we departed, heading farther south toward the Negev. As we traveled, we passed through the Canaanite towns of Jerusalem and Bethlehem. They were not significant places.

Bethlehem, I later learned, was named after a Canaanite fertility god. Neither town seemed to have strategic or economic importance, but something told me that someday they would. As a matter of fact, as I looked at the hills of Bethlehem, I couldn't shake the feeling that it would one day play an important role in God's plan for me ... the great nation that would descend from me ... and through them *all* the families of the earth.

A severe famine was spreading across the land. I sent my servants ahead to find a location that would provide us with resources to weather the famine. They found that the best place for refuge was in Egypt. Something told me this wouldn't be the last time that I or my descendants would seek refuge in Egypt.

But I was certain that the Egyptians would covet my wealth and my beautiful wife and seek to kill me. I trusted God to lead us in our journey, but I did not trust Him enough to protect me in Egypt. So, I decided on a plan before we entered their borders.

"You are a woman beautiful in appearance," I said to Sarai, *"and when the Egyptians see you, they will say, 'This is his wife.' Then they will kill me, but they will let you live. Therefore, say you are my sister, that it may go well with me because of you, and that my life may be spared for your sake."*(4)

When we arrived in Egypt, the Egyptians reacted exactly as I expected. When the princes of pharaoh saw Sarai and heard she was my sister, they took her into pharaoh's palace. He lavished me with great gifts of sheep, oxen, camels, donkeys, and servants. My plan was working well!

That is, until the Lord afflicted pharaoh and his house with great plagues, and his magicians helped him discover that Sarai was my wife. But pharaoh feared Jehovah God and chose to send us away instead of killing me. And to my greater surprise, he allowed me to take all of the possessions he had given me.

We returned to where I had built the altar between Bethel and Ai. My nephew Lot decided to journey east and dwell in the Jordan Valley while I remained in that place, living in peace among the Canaanites and Perizzites.

After Lot departed, the Lord again came to me and said, *"Lift up your eyes and look from the place where you are, northward and southward and eastward and westward, for all the land that you see I will give to you and to your offspring forever. I will make your offspring as the dust of the earth, so that if one can count the dust of the earth, your offspring also can be counted. Arise, walk through the length and the breadth of the land, for I will give it to you."*[5]

I had wealth. I had a beautiful wife. I had many servants. I lived in a lush land. I had everything I could ever want … except a son. How could I possibly have offspring as numerous as the dust of the earth if I first did not have a son?

We had now been living in the land of Canaan for ten years. Sarai knew my longing and we shared the pain of being childless. Again, rather than trust God, we decided to take matters into our own hands. Sarai had a female servant by the name of Hagar, whom pharaoh had given her in Egypt.

Sarai said to me, *"The Lord has prevented me from bearing children. Go in to my servant; it may be that I shall obtain children by her."*[6] So I did as Sarai said, and Hagar conceived. When I was eighty-six years old, Hagar bore me a son whom I named Ishmael. But Hagar and my son quickly became contemptible in the eyes of my wife.

When I was ninety-nine, God again came to me and said, *"No longer shall your name be called Abram, but your name shall be Abraham, for I have made you the father of a multitude of nations. I will make you exceedingly fruitful, and I will make you into nations, and kings shall come from you. And I will establish My covenant between Me and you and your offspring after you throughout their generations for an everlasting covenant, to be God to you and to your offspring after you. And I will give to you and to your offspring after you the land of your sojournings, all the land of Canaan, for an everlasting possession, and I will be their God."*[7]

God instructed me that as a sign of the covenant between Him, me, and my offspring that would follow – "every male who is eight days old will be circumcised, whether he is born as offspring or brought into your home as a servant. And any male who is not circumcised will be cut off from his people because he has broken covenant with Me."[8]

Then God continued, *"As for Sarai your wife, you shall not call her name Sarai, but Sarah shall be her name. I will bless her, and moreover, I will give you a son by her. I will bless her, and she shall become nations; kings of peoples shall come from her."*[9]

You can imagine my reaction – I laughed! Sarah laughed! How could a man of one hundred years and a woman of ninety years possibly bear a child? But God was not laughing! He said, "At this time next year, Sarah will bear you a son and his name will be Isaac – and I will establish My covenant with him."[10]

That very day, in obedience to my Lord's command, I entered into that covenant with Jehovah God. I took Ishmael and all of my male servants – and we were all circumcised. One year later, my son Isaac was born. Sarah and I both laughed again. But this time it was joyful laughter! God had given us a son in our old age!

With the birth of Isaac, I think I finally realized I could trust God to fulfill His promises. He is trustworthy. He is not a Man who lies – like me. He is not a Man who is limited in His ability – like me. He is not a Man who is unable to see into the future – like me. He is the sovereign Almighty God! What He promises He is able to fulfill! And what He promises He *will* fulfill! My part is simply to trust Him – with my whole heart, soul, and mind!

It wasn't long before my trust was again put to the test. On the day Isaac was weaned, Sarah came to me and demanded that I cast out Hagar and Ishmael from our camp. I knew that Isaac was my son of God's promise and my heir, but Ishmael was still my son. In the midst of my turmoil, God gave me a promise, *"I will make a nation of the son of the slave woman also, because he is your offspring."*[11] God told me to do as Sarah was demanding, and the next morning as I sent off Ishmael and Hagar, I knew that I could trust their safekeeping to God. He had promised ... and He would fulfill it.

It was several years before my faith and trust were again put to the test. Isaac was in his teens. God called out to me and said, *"Take your son Isaac, whom you love, and go to the land of Moriah, and offer him there as a burnt offering on one of the mountains of which I shall tell you."*[12]

So, Isaac and I, together with two servants, arose early the next morning and made our way south toward the city of Jerusalem to the mount of Moriah. On the third day of our travels, I looked up and saw the place that God was directing us to go.

At the base of the mountain, I instructed the servants to wait. Isaac and I would go alone the rest of the way. I laid the wood for the burnt offering on Isaac's shoulders to carry, and I brought the fire and the knife. As we climbed the mount, Isaac turned and asked me, *"My father, behold, the fire and the wood, but where is the lamb for a burnt offering?"*[13]

I will confess that I didn't quite know how to answer to my son. I was walking in obedience to Jehovah God – my Father – and I would trust Him. I said the only thing I knew to say, *"God will provide for Himself the lamb for a burnt offering, my son."*[14]

My son was satisfied with my answer because he trusted me. When we reached the place God had shown me, I built the altar and prepared the wood for the fire. Even as I bound my son, he trusted me. He never struggled – and he could have very easily overpowered me. He didn't even question me when I laid him on the altar.

My heart was in my throat as I raised my knife above my son. This was my son – the son through whom God had promised that all nations would be blessed. Did God intend to bless the nations through his death as a sin offering on this altar? My heart ached – but I had learned that I must trust God.

Just as I raised my hand to plunge the knife into my son's heart, an angel of the Lord called out to me from heaven saying, *"Abraham, Abraham! Do not lay your hand on the boy or do anything to him, for now I know that you fear God, seeing you have not withheld your son."*(15)

As I looked up, I saw a ram caught by his horns in a thicket. The ram hadn't been there a moment ago. I reached down and embraced my son. I removed his bindings and together we bound the ram and offered the sacrifice to Jehovah God.

The angel of the Lord again called out and said, *"Because you have done this and have not withheld your son, your offspring will possess the gate of his enemies and in your offspring shall all the nations of the earth be blessed."*(16)

It was then I realized God would truly provide the lamb as a sacrifice for our sin. But not just any lamb. It would be His Lamb – the only Lamb truly worthy to be slain. And He would present His Lamb at just the right moment and at just the right place – perhaps this very place in the land of Moriah. He had asked me if I was willing to sacrifice my only son of promise. Was God preparing to sacrifice His only Son of promise? And yet I feared His hand would not be stilled. His Sacrifice would be given. His Sacrifice would bless all the nations. And His Sacrifice would be given through my offspring.

With a heavy heart, I had climbed the mount that morning with my son. Now I descended the mount with a heart that was still heavy. My son had not been sacrificed on that day ... but one day a Son would be sacrificed on that mount. He would be a Son who also would be born somewhat unexpectedly in an unusual way. He would be born of a promise. And He, too, would one day willingly climb that mount.

· · ·

Isaac had witnessed the promise. He would tell his offspring the promise. They would tell their offspring. And the promise would be passed from one generation to the next.

Little did I know when the promised One would come. Little did I know how He would come. But I knew He *would* come …

DAVID – THE SHEPHERD KING

*M*y name is David. I was a shepherd in my youth and in many respects I still am. I am the youngest son of Jesse, who was the grandson of Boaz and Ruth. I was the runt of the litter. My family expected great things from my brothers, but they expected very little from me.

As a matter of fact, when the prophet Samuel came to Bethlehem to anoint a king from the sons of my father, I was left in the Bethlehem hills to watch over our sheep. There was no need for me to be brought home. Everyone was certain I could never be the king of Israel.

Over eight hundred years have passed since my ancestor Abraham took his son Isaac to the top of Mount Moriah as God instructed. Much has occurred in those years. Isaac grew up to have two sons – Esau and Jacob. Jacob tricked his older brother out of his birthright and became the next patriarch of our people. As a result, God renamed him Israel. Jehovah God permitted events to unfold in such a way that Jacob's second-to-youngest son, Joseph, became the prime minister of Egypt under the rule of King Merneferre Ay I.

. . .

Famine had again spread throughout the land of Canaan, and for a second time Egypt became a place of refuge – this time through the esteemed position of Joseph. Jacob and the remainder of his family settled in Egypt and there they multiplied into the great nation that God had promised Abraham. However, their numbers frightened their Egyptian hosts, so a pharaoh who did not remember Joseph made the Israelites slaves.

But four hundred thirty years after the day Abraham had first sought refuge in Egypt, the people of Israel were led out of the bondage of Egyptian slavery by Jehovah God through His prophet Moses. A family had entered the land, but a nation of about two million people made their exodus. God was delivering His people into a land He had promised to Abraham. Due to their faithless disobedience, the Israelites ended up wandering in the wilderness for forty years before God permitted them to enter their Promised Land.

Possessing the land wasn't easy. It required faith and courage – but our God was ever faithful. As long as the people kept their eyes on Him, the Lord gave them victory over their enemies – but disobedience always brought about defeat. Even to this day, there are enemies that remain in the land.

Soon after the prophet Samuel anointed me to become king, our people were again being attacked by the Philistines. Our men had gathered in the Valley of Elah and were being taunted by the Philistines' champion – a giant of a man called Goliath, who stood just under ten feet tall. My three oldest brothers were a part of our army there in the valley under the leadership of our King Saul.

For forty days Goliath dared our army to put forth a champion to fight him – and for forty days no one stepped forward. It was embarrassing! The people of Jehovah God were cowering in front of this pagan. It had been the fear of giants that caused our people to wander in the wilderness for forty years – and here we were still trembling before giants. We needed the courage of our ancestor Caleb to trust God and stand up to this giant!

. . .

On the forty-first day, my father sent me to bring food to my brothers. As I greeted them, the Philistine again stepped forward and issued his challenge. As I watched, all of our men, including my brothers, shuddered in fear. I turned to the men standing beside me and said, *"Who is this uncircumcised Philistine, that he should defy the armies of the living God?"*[1]

Word made its way to King Saul that I was prepared to go and fight the Philistine. As the king looked at me in disbelief, I stood before him and said, *"The Lord who delivered me from the paw of the lion and from the paw of the bear will deliver me from the hand of this Philistine."*[2]

The king tried to get me to wear his armor and carry his sword into battle. But they were too cumbersome and heavy – and not what the Lord intended. So, I approached the giant with only the weapons of a shepherd – my staff, my sling, and my shepherd's pouch. Along the way I chose five smooth stones from the brook and put them in my pouch.

You may be wondering why I chose *five* stones. I believed with my whole heart that Almighty God was leading me to confront this Philistine. I was confident He would give me victory. My trust was in Him, not in the stones. I trusted God to defeat the giant with one stone, but I also wanted to be prepared if any of his comrades attacked me. At that moment, I wasn't certain the Israelite army would come to my defense if the need arose.

The giant taunted me as he watched me approach. As I ran toward him, I released a stone from my sling. Its trajectory was true, and it struck him in an unprotected spot on his forehead. The stone sank deep into his skull, and as it did, he fell on his face to the ground. The earth shook as he came crashing down.

. . .

Everyone in both camps stood motionless. They could not believe their eyes. I ran to his fallen body, removed his sword from its sheath, and cut off his head with a single slash of the blade.

When the Philistines grasped the reality that their champion was dead, they fled in every direction. Our men then rose with a shout and pursued them as far as the gates of Gath and Ekron. And I brought the head of the giant to my king. God had surely granted His people victory that day!

But two more things occurred that day that were more subtle – and more lasting. The seed of a loving friendship was planted in the hearts of King Saul's son, Jonathan, and me. From that day forward our souls were knit together. But also, a seed of jealousy was birthed in the heart of my king. The accolades people extended to me angered and displeased him.

In the months and years that followed, I witnessed the hatred and evil that jealousy can breed. And there is no greater jealousy than that of a king. But I also realized that my king was afraid of me – because he knew that Jehovah God was with me.

The king wanted me dead, but he knew I must die by the hand of the Philistines. The people would turn away from King Saul if injury came to me from his hand. So, he devised a plan. The king offered to give his daughter, Merab, in marriage to me if I would fight the Philistines. However, I considered myself unworthy to marry the eldest daughter of a king, so I declined his offer.

After a while, I became aware that the king's second daughter, Michal, was attracted to me – as I was to her. But I was still a poor shepherd who could little afford the bride price for a king's daughter. The king sent word to me that the only bride price he desired was one hundred fore-skins of the king's enemies – the Philistines. He was secretly confident that I would be killed in the attempt to gather the bounty he required.

· · ·

Desiring his daughter's hand, I went out with the soldiers under my command. However, we did not slay one hundred Philistines – we doubled that number. And I returned to the king with a double portion of the bride price. The king reluctantly gave me his daughter as my wife. God had again blessed me greatly. I knew it, and so did the king. And he became even more fearful and jealous of me.

The chronicles of the kings recorded the many victories that God gave me over the Philistines. They also recorded King Saul's many attempts to kill me. Often those attempts were foiled by the king's own children. Eventually, I became estranged by my king and was forced to remain outside of his grasp. He even took Michal away from me while I was gone from her and gave her to another.

But that which the king endeavored to take from me, my Lord repaid to me out of His goodness and His grace. Many – including my brothers – who observed the king's actions toward me became discontented with him and began to gather around me under my command. And their numbers grew each day.

Soon the king made no pretense about his intent to kill me, including the day he had all of the priests of Nob put to death, as well as their women, children, and livestock – simply for giving me provisions for my journey. His hatred toward me now waxed hot.

One day he sought me out in the sheepfolds of the wilderness of Engedi. Several of my men and I were resting in the innermost parts of a cave. In the providence of God, the king chose to enter into the outermost part of that cave in order to relieve himself. My men told me that the Lord had delivered my enemy into my hands. But to the contrary, I believed the Lord would not have me raise a hand against the one He had anointed to be king.

Instead, I simply cut off a corner of his robe. Then, after the king left the cave, I followed him out. When we were a safe distance apart, I called out to him. With the piece of his robe in my hand, I said, "I spared you, though some told me to kill you. There is no treason in my heart or hands. I have not sinned against you, and my hand shall not be against you."[3]

King Saul replied, *"You are more righteous than I, for you have repaid me good, whereas I have repaid you evil. And now I know that you shall surely be king, and the kingdom of Israel shall be established in your hand."*[4]

That wasn't the last time my Lord led me to spare the life of my king, even though he continued to try to destroy me. But one day, on Mount Gilboa, the Philistines overtook King Saul and his sons, including my beloved Jonathan. The king was mortally wounded by archers and chose to fall upon his own sword rather than be ravaged by his enemies. The Philistines celebrated their victory over the men of Israel that day and desecrated the bodies of the king and his sons.

When I heard of their deaths, I mourned deeply. King Saul had been the Lord's anointed and Jonathan had been even closer than a brother to me. There was absolutely no sense of satisfaction over their deaths.

Our people divided that day. I was thirty years old when the people of Judah in the south anointed me as their king. The people of Israel to the north, led by Abner, the commander of King Saul's army, took the king's son, Ish-bosheth, and made him king. We remained hostile with one another for seven and one-half years. Then by the mercies of God, He reunited His people as one kingdom and I became king over all. Many died in the process, including Ish-bosheth and Abner, though neither died at my hand – and I grieved both of their deaths.

But the time had come to live as a united kingdom. One of my first acts as king was to lead our men to capture the city of Jerusalem from the Jebusites. It became known as the City of David and it was here that I established my palace. The following year, I pitched a tent in Jerusalem at the top of the mount where Abraham had brought his son Isaac. I had the

Ark of the Lord's Covenant placed in the tent. Just as the Lord had been present that day with Abraham and Isaac, He would now always be present in this place. The Ark would remain in that tent until a proper temple could be built.

The Lord told me through the prophet Nathan, *"I have not lived in a house since the day I brought up the people of Israel from Egypt to this day, but I have been moving about in a tent for My dwelling. David, I took you from the pasture, from following the sheep, that you should be prince over My people Israel. And I have been with you wherever you went and have cut off all your enemies from before you. And I will make for you a great name, like the name of the great ones of the earth. And I will appoint a place for My people Israel and will plant them, so that they may dwell in their own place and be disturbed no more. And violent men shall afflict them no more.*

"Moreover, I declare to you that I will make you a house. When your days are fulfilled and you lie down with your fathers, I will raise up your offspring after you, who shall come from your body, and I will establish his kingdom. He shall build a house for My name, and I will establish the throne of his kingdom forever. I will be to him a Father, and he shall be to me a son. When he commits iniquity, I will discipline him with the rod of men, with the stripes of the sons of men, but My steadfast love will not depart from him, as I took it from Saul, whom I put away from before you. And your house and your kingdom shall be made sure forever before Me. Your throne shall be established forever."[5]

I would not build the temple. That task would be left for my son to complete. But my throne – actually the Lord's throne – was now to be established forever! Jehovah God will make sure of it. He will establish the throne of His kingdom forever. His steadfast love will not depart from us. The Lord has promised that He has established His throne through me – a simple shepherd from Bethlehem.

But one day the Lord will say to One who is much greater than I: *"My Lord, sit at My right hand, until I make Your enemies Your footstool." The Lord sends forth from Zion Your mighty scepter. Rule in the midst of Your enemies! Your people will offer themselves freely on the day of Your pow-*

er, in holy garments; from the womb of the morning, the dew of Your youth will be Yours. The Lord has sworn and will not change His mind, "You are a Priest forever after the order of Melchizedek." The Lord is at Your right hand; He will shatter kings on the day of His wrath. He will execute judgment among the nations. He will drink from the brook by the way; therefore He will lift up His head. [6]

Little did I know when my Lord would come to sit on His throne. Little did I know God would raise up another shepherd from Bethlehem. Little did I know how He would establish His forever Priest and His forever kingdom. But I knew what God had promised, He would bring about ...

~

ISAIAH – THE PROPHET

I am Isaiah, the son of Amoz, who was a son of King Joash of Judah. My father's eldest brother, Amaziah, was heir to the throne and became king when my grandfather died. My father grew up as a prince of Judah enjoying the comforts and privileges of the royal court in Jerusalem. I also enjoyed a privileged life within the courts of the king. King Uzziah was my cousin and though he was forty years my senior, I loved him dearly.

When my cousin died, I saw a vision of the Lord God Jehovah sitting on His mighty throne with the train of His robe filling the temple. I was overwhelmed by my sinfulness as I stood in God's holy presence. But on that day, He sent me forth to be His messenger to His people.

I was still a young man. Though I was aware of my own inadequacy, I had no idea what being the messenger of God would mean. I did not know how it would impact my familial relationships. But what I did know was I could not be disobedient to the call of God.

At that time, over two hundred sixty years had passed since my ancestor, King David, had ruled. Our nation, under the reign of his son, King

Solomon, had prospered and was respected by all the nations. But when King Solomon died, our nation again split in two – just as it had when King Saul died. We divided into the northern kingdom of Israel and the southern kingdom of Judah. The days of lasting peace and prosperity ended with the split. Nation turned against nation. And our enemies turned against both of us.

That split was not only a political divide, but it also reflected that our people had turned away from God. There was a succession of kings in the northern kingdom who have done evil in the sight of the Lord from the day of the separation until today. And our kingdom of Judah was not exempt from evil, either. We also had a succession of kings who did evil in the sight of God.

Gratefully, my grandfather, King Joash, who began ruling at the age of seven, sought to do what was pleasing in the eyes of the Lord. That was true of my uncle, King Amaziah; my cousin, King Uzziah; and his son, King Jotham. I was the messenger of God under Jotham's sixteen-year rule as he sought to lead our people to honor and obey God. I continued to warn his successor, King Ahaz, of the growing threat from Assyria. But Ahaz, unlike his father, did evil in the eyes of the Lord throughout his sixteen-year rule and disregarded the word of the Lord.

By God's grace, King Hezekiah, the son of Ahaz, turned from his father's wicked ways and led us in righteousness before God. I watched with gratitude and pride as my daughter became Hezekiah's queen – and as our nation began to turn back to God. God honored my son-in-law's faithfulness and sent His angel to strike down the attacking Assyrians, causing them to scatter and return to their own land in shame.

After Hezekiah reigned for fourteen years, he became deathly ill. God sent me to tell my son-in-law to set his affairs in order for he was going to die. *"You will not recover from this illness,"*[1] I told him. But Hezekiah beseeched the Lord with great earnest, and God showed him mercy.

· · ·

Before I had even left the royal courtyard, God told me to return to Hezekiah and tell him, *"This is what the Lord, the God of your ancestor David, says: 'I have heard your prayer and seen your tears. I will heal you, and three days from now you will get out of bed and go to the Temple of the Lord. I will add fifteen years to your life, and I will rescue you and this city from the king of Assyria. I will defend this city for My own honor and for the sake of My servant David.'"*[2]

God gave Hezekiah a sign that He would do what He had promised. He caused the shadow of the sundial to move ten degrees backward. God added forty minutes to that day to assure Hezekiah of His promise. Until that day, God had not demonstrated His power over time since He had stilled the sun and the moon to permit the Israelites to defeat the Amorites under the leadership of Joshua.[3]

He did so for Hezekiah by His grace, and He added those fifteen years to Hezekiah's life. Unfortunately, it became a reminder for us to be careful what we ask God to do on our behalf. Soon afterward, my daughter conceived a son by Hezekiah. My grandson's name is Manasseh. And when Manasseh became king following his father's death, he did evil in the sight of the Lord, leading our people to turn away from God.

My grandson will not heed the word of the Lord from me – even though he is but a lad in his early teens. There are many who believe he is plotting to have me killed. But regardless, I will continue to bear witness to him as I have to the three kings before him.

I have seen the sons of David in a way most have not. I have grown up in their presence. I have been part of their family. I have brought them counsel from Almighty God. I have seen that counsel accepted, and I have seen it rejected. I have seen clearly why God grieved over the rejection of His people when they cried out to Samuel for a king.[4]

But God granted their request, in some ways, just like he granted Hezekiah's request to add years to his life. God knew they had no idea what they were asking for. But He also knew He would ultimately accomplish His divine purpose no matter what the people chose.

God began to show me that He is the Creator of all people – not only the people of Israel and Judah. His plan is to redeem not only a nation, but His fallen creation back to Himself. And His plan of redemption will be through the Messiah – the Promised One He will send. The Messiah will be part of the lineage of David through the succession of these kings – even those who did evil in His sight. His plan will be accomplished. Even the disobedience of kings cannot hinder it.

God gave me this message for His people:

> *"I have a plan for the whole earth, a hand of judgment upon all the nations.*
> *The Lord of Heaven's Armies has spoken – who can change His plans? When His hand is raised, who can stop Him?"*[5]

God's plan will not be thwarted, and it will be carried out in a most unlikely way. His plan is to send One who will know sorrow. He will cleanse us of our unrighteousness, just as He cleansed my lips with a burning coal.

> *"Who has believed our message? To whom has the Lord revealed His powerful arm?*
> *My Servant grew up in the Lord's presence like a tender green shoot, like a root in dry ground. There was nothing beautiful or majestic about His appearance, nothing to attract us to Him.*
> *He was despised and rejected – a Man of sorrows, acquainted with deepest grief.*
> *We turned our backs on Him and looked the other way. He was despised, and we did not care.*
> *Yet it was our weaknesses He carried; it was our sorrows that weighed Him down. And we thought His troubles were a punishment from God, a punishment for His own sins!*
> *But He was pierced for our rebellion, crushed for our sins. He was beaten so we could be whole. He was whipped so we could be healed.*

All of us, like sheep, have strayed away. We have left God's paths to follow our own. Yet the Lord laid on Him the sins of us all."[5]

And how will He come? He will come as a baby:

"For a Child is born to us, a son is given to us.
The government will rest on His shoulders.
And He will be called: Wonderful Counselor, Mighty God, Everlasting Father,
Prince of Peace. His government and its peace will never end. He will rule with
fairness and justice from the throne of His ancestor David for all eternity. The
passionate commitment of the Lord of Heaven's Armies will make this
happen!"[6]

He will be born of a virgin:

"The Lord Himself will give you the sign. Look! The virgin will conceive a Child!
She will give birth to a Son and will call Him Immanuel (which means 'God is
with us')."[7]

And the Messiah will reign forever and ever as the King of kings and the Lord of lords. God's message to us is a message of judgment and hope. God will send One who will save His people, but He will also judge His people. And He will do miraculous works:

"When He comes, He will open the eyes of the blind and unplug the ears of the deaf.
The lame will leap like a deer, and those who cannot speak will sing for joy!"[8]

The Lord God Jehovah has permitted me to be the messenger of His Good News to all people. He has permitted me to hear and see that which will one day come to pass. God promised our patriarch, Abraham, that the nations will be blessed through his seed. He promised my ancestor, David, that the King of kings will sit on his throne. And now He has permitted me to see how He will come.

Little did I know, however, the full extent of the majesty and glory of the One who will one day come ...

MALACHI – THE MESSENGER

*M*y name is Malachi, and I am a third-generation returnee to Jerusalem. God has set me apart to be His messenger.

Slightly more than one hundred years after the prophet Isaiah died, the people of Judah were taken into captivity by the Babylonians. About fifty years later, Babylon fell to the Persians under the rule of King Cyrus the Great. King Cyrus respected our customs and beliefs, as he did the practices of all the various peoples who were subjects of his empire.

He determined that our places of worship must be restored. Accordingly, he commissioned a contingent of our people to return to Jerusalem to rebuild the temple. He sent Zerubbabel – the grandson of the last king of Judah – to lead the effort and designated him as the new governor of what was then the small province of Judah. My grandfather was one of the men who accompanied Zerubbabel.

Completion of what is now considered to be the Second Temple took about five years. Even when my father was born here in Jerusalem a few years later, our city continued to be a shadow of its former glory days. For the most part, the city was in a state of disrepair with a population of less than two thousand people. Little attention was paid to the province of Judah by our Persian rulers in Susa for many years, until an Amalekite named Haman became prime minister under the rule of King Xerxes.

Haman was a descendant of Agag, the king of the Amalekites. The Amalekites had initiated an unprovoked attack against our people many years ago in the wilderness. God had given our people victory that day as Moses held up his staff on a hill overlooking the battle while his brothers held up his arms. And God had continued to give us victory over them through King David.

Their hatred for our people had remained strong ever since. Haman believed it was now his destiny to retaliate and destroy our people once and for all. He issued a decree throughout the empire, sealed with the king's signet ring, that all Jews were to be slaughtered on a single day – March 7 of the following year.

When the messengers arrived in Jerusalem announcing the decree, the entire city was overwhelmed with despair. According to this new law, our people were to be annihilated and we would not be permitted to defend ourselves. Fear led to mourning, which led to complete resignation. Our people believed nothing could be done, and that Jehovah God had abandoned us. They began to do whatever was right in their own eyes. Corruption permeated the city as they turned away from God.

All would have been lost had it not been for our God and His strategic placement of two people in the court of King Xerxes. The first was Queen Esther. Her name at birth had been Hadassah, and she was a daughter of Judah from the tribe of Benjamin. Prior to the event I am about to describe, the king had no idea of his queen's Jewish bloodline. But Esther boldly approached the king on behalf of all the Jews at great risk to herself and disclosed Haman's evil plot to him.

God opened the king's eyes to Haman's deception and evil intent, prompting the king to order Haman's public execution. There was a scribe in the king's court by the name of Mordecai, who was also Queen Esther's older cousin. When the king heard of Mordecai's heroic actions to thwart an earlier plot by Haman to assassinate the king, he honored Mordecai by elevating him to the position of prime minister.

The king then issued a decree through his new prime minister giving the Jews authority to defend themselves. Sensing the king's earnestness to protect the Jewish people, all of the commanders throughout the provinces – in a show of support – decided to take up arms to defend the Jews and annihilate those who attempted to harm them.

Our people's celebration was heard throughout Jerusalem and the entire Persian Empire. As a result, there was a revival among our people and a renewed devotion to God and His law throughout the empire. Regrettably, that devotion was short-lived in the city of Jerusalem. Generations of pagan worship and disregard for God's law continued to cloud the judgment of the people of our city.

I was born in Jerusalem about the time of this failed attempt to annihilate our people. As I grew up, I was taught the history of our people, but I was taught very little by my father and grandfather about our religious beliefs. Our religious practices aligned more with the pagan practices that surrounded us.

Because of the great influence of Queen Esther and Mordecai on King Xerxes, our people enjoyed greater religious freedoms than we had experienced since captivity. This prompted a renewed interest among our religious leaders in Susa to safeguard the teachings of Moses and the prophets. Mordecai and others established an assembly of leaders, rabbis, and prophets called the Great Synagogue.

The purpose of the assembly was to safeguard the Torah and other sacred writings of the prophets, canonizing them into Scripture. These leaders also were to teach the people about our God and His covenant with us.

The assembly remained in Susa and over the years began to include such people as Ezra and Nehemiah.

Artaxerxes, the son of Xerxes, was even more influenced by his father's queen, Esther. Her presence in the royal household while he was growing up had great effect on the shaping of his character. When he became king, he commissioned Ezra to go to Jerusalem to lead in a spiritual, moral, and social restoration of the temple. He was to build on the work that Zerub-babel began.

Ezra led a large contingent of exiles from Susa for that purpose. To his dismay, when he arrived in Jerusalem he discovered the spiritual climate among the majority of our people was worse than he had imagined. It was tepid at best, if not antagonistic toward anything having to do with Jehovah God.

Numerous men had married non-Jewish women and had adopted the beliefs of their wives' culture. A deep hostility quickly developed between those who had just arrived from Susa and the families who had never left Jerusalem, as well as the larger number of those, like my family, who had returned several generations earlier.

I was a young man in my early twenties when Ezra arrived, and I clearly recall his despair over what he encountered. I will never forget the day he tore his clothes and fell to his knees in the middle of the road as an expression of grief over the sins of God's people, confessing their sins before Jehovah God.

Until that day, I had been proud of my heritage and grateful for a grandfather and father who had been willing to return to our land to rebuild it. But I had never witnessed the deep convictions Ezra was demonstrating toward Jehovah God. That day, I saw something in him that I wanted to have. I wanted to love God wholeheartedly and obey Him as earnestly as Ezra.

. . .

Ezra was steadfast in his mission to restore the temple and purify our community from the immoral customs of the land. He was determined to obey the law of God and to teach those laws to the people. Day after day, I saw him brave the opposition – some days in victory and other days in defeat.

By the time I was in my mid-thirties, a new governor arrived in Jerusalem. His name was Nehemiah. He was sent by Xerxes with the mandate to rebuild the walls of our city. The walls had been in disrepair since their destruction by the Babylonians. Our people had made their homes in the midst of those crumbling walls for over seventy years and had become quite complacent about them.

It reflected the lack of pride and concern our people had for our city – once the center of our religious worship and our nation. Nehemiah was determined that if Jerusalem was again going to be the City of David – the capital of our province – the walls needed to be restored.

Nehemiah encountered opposition, just as Ezra had – perhaps even more. Some among us were resistant to this change. They had profited – in power and wealth – from our despair, and they quickly began to voice their opposition to Nehemiah and his plan. But he remained steadfast. I admired his resolve and his passion!

Each of us was given a specific task for rebuilding a portion of the wall. And in just fifty-two days it was finished! When our enemies and the naysayers saw and heard what happened, they were frightened and humiliated. They knew this work had been done with the help of our God! But rather than repent, they were silent as they waited for another opportunity to regain their influence and power.

The following week, Nehemiah directed Ezra to read the Book of the Law to the people. The priest stood on a high wooden platform, reading from early morning until noon. My people chanted, "Amen! Amen!" as we lifted our hands toward heaven. Then we bowed down and worshiped the Lord with our faces to the ground.[(1)]

As Ezra read Scripture, we discovered that God had commanded through Moses that these very days be set aside as an observance of the Festival of Tabernacles commemorating the forty-year journey of our people in the wilderness and God's faithfulness to His people. So, we immediately stopped everything and entered into that observance. We recounted the deliverance by our God. But we also remembered the sins of our people – and our own sin. Then we renewed our covenant with God.

Nehemiah and Ezra decided the assembly of the Great Synagogue needed to relocate here in Jerusalem. We would continue the work that began in Susa. It was appropriate that the safeguarding of Scripture, the teachings of the holy feasts, and the recording of the oral law be done here. I was deeply humbled and honored when Nehemiah and Ezra invited me to be part of the assembly. But when my friend and mentor Ezra died, my heart ached. His absence would be keenly felt among our people.

We began to look at Nehemiah not only as our governor, but also as a shepherd to guide us in the ways of the Lord. Though the priests in the temple carried out their sacred duties, it was Nehemiah who was our spiritual leader. But the arrival of a messenger from Susa signaled that everything was about to change. After having served as governor for twelve years, Nehemiah was being summoned by King Xerxes to return to Susa.

I grieved as I watched how quickly our people turned back to their old ways after Nehemiah departed. I couldn't help but remember how Ezra had torn his clothes and fallen prostrate before God just twenty-five years earlier. That was exactly how I felt. The grief that God must be experiencing was coursing through my veins. Even the priests in the temple were turning back to their former corrupt practices.

.   .   .

One morning, I heard the voice of God say, "Malachi, you will be My messenger. You will declare My message of judgment to the people. You will rebuke their wicked practices, their hypocrisy, their infidelity, their arrogance and their false worship. My people have again become so sinful that My words no longer have any impact on them.

"You will tell them that they have robbed Me by cheating Me of the tithes and offerings that are due Me.[2] Tell them they have dishonored Me by making marital vows before Me that they have broken.[3] They have said terrible things about Me and demonstrated them in their lack of obedience.[4]

"Tell them the Lord Almighty says, *'The day of judgment is coming burning like a furnace. The arrogant and the wicked will be burned up like straw on that day. But for you who fear My Name, the Son of Righteousness will rise with healing in His wings.'*[5]

"And I will send a messenger who will clear the way before the One I promised through My prophet, Isaiah. You will not hear from Me again until the messenger I am sending comes. Watch for him. Listen for him. *His preaching will turn the hearts of parents to their children, and the hearts of children to their parents."*[6]

I realized this message was not only for those within the sound of my voice, but a message for all people to heed until His Promised One comes. Despite the disobedience of His people time and again throughout our history, God has been faithful. He has a plan to save us from the judgment that is due us. He will by no means clear the guilty or ignore our sin. But He will make a way so we can be saved from our iniquity. Our Savior is coming! We must watch for the messenger who will come before Him.

Little did I know when that day would be – but I knew that He would come in His perfect timing ...

∾

GABRIEL – THE ANGEL

I am an angel created by Almighty God to be His messenger. My name is Gabriel. *"I stand in the very presence of God."*[(1)] He gave me my name, which means "God is my strength." My comings and goings are at His command. I only speak the words He has given me to say. I stand beside the archangel Michael as his support and defense.[(2)] For millennia, God has used me to deliver His message to His creation, but it never fails to amaze me how His creation receives – or in some instances, refuses to receive – His message.

Michael and I accompanied the Lord when He visited Abraham near the oak grove at Mamre to announce that Sarah would bear a son.[(3)] I heard Sarah laugh in response to the word of my Lord. He rightfully rebuked her by saying, *"Is anything too hard for the Lord?"*[(4)]

God was preparing to raise up His chosen people from Abraham's offspring. They would be a people through whom God would make His name known. The stench of wickedness that the Lord destroyed through the flood was again beginning to rise across the earth. Nowhere was that stench greater than in the city of Sodom.

. . .

Almighty God sent Michael and me from Mamre to the city of Sodom to destroy it. But the Lord briefly remained in Mamre because He had decided to disclose His plans to Abraham. When he heard the Lord's plan, Abraham interceded on behalf of his nephew, Lot, who lived in the city. In His mercy and grace, God agreed to withhold destruction of Sodom if there were ten righteous men within the city.[5]

However, when we arrived in Sodom we found every man in the city blinded by his sin, except Lot. We seized his hand, and those of his wife and daughters, and rushed them to safety outside the city. Then the Lord rained down fire on Sodom and the surrounding cities and villages, eliminating all life – people, plants, and animals alike. Sadly, Lot's wife perished because she disobediently looked back at the destruction and became a pillar of salt. But God had honored His promise to Abraham and kept Lot safe.

I can bear witness to the unchanging nature of Almighty God – whatever He promises will come about. It was true in the destruction of Sodom. It was true in the saving of Lot. It would be true in the nation that would arise from Abraham. And it would be true in His ultimate plan to redeem this lost world.

Over thirteen hundred years later, the Lord again sent me on a mission to help one of His servants. Most of God's chosen people had turned their backs on Him, and they were now being held captive by the Babylonians. But a remnant of those who were righteous remained. One of those was His servant Daniel. God had given Daniel a vision of what would take place in the last days before He returned to judge the earth.

But Daniel did not know what the vision meant so he began to pray for understanding. God sent me to reveal what was going to happen.[7] It would be a time of anguish. It would be a time of sacrilege and desecration. It would be a time when evil seemed to prevail. But, at that moment, when everything will appear to be at its darkest, God will return to establish His kingdom on this earth. On that day, all creation will be judged.

The wicked will enter into their punishment, and the redeemed will receive their inheritance.

But before that day of judgment takes place, God will send His Redeemer – the One He spoke of even in the Garden of Eden, the One He promised through the seed of Abraham, the One He foretold through His prophet Isaiah, and the One whose arrival was anticipated by His prophet Malachi.

Almost six hundred years later, God again sent me. But this time, I was sent to tell some of His servants some very startling news – the day of the Redeemer's coming had arrived.

A priest named Zechariah was in the sanctuary of the temple in Jerusalem burning incense on the altar before the Lord. He had never entered the sanctuary before that day, and he would never do so again. It was a once-in-a-lifetime honor to present the offering of incense before the Lord. The priest was an old man in his late seventies. He had served as a priest for a long time, and now his opportunity to do this had come. It was obvious – and understandable – that he was caught up in the awe of the moment!

In the blink of an eye, I appeared before him on the right side of the altar. I was facing the priest with my back to the veil that separated the sanctuary from the Holy of Holies. To say the least, the priest was startled by my appearance. No one else was in the sanctuary with him and I had just appeared out of nowhere.

Also, I had just come from being in the presence of Almighty God. Do you remember how Moses' face radiated the shekinah glory after he spent extended time with Jehovah God? That same glory radiates from and surrounds those of us who are angels who stand in Almighty God's presence. So, not only did I appear out of nowhere, I glowed. Zechariah was visibly shaken and overwhelmed with fear.

· · ·

I said to him, *"Don't be afraid, Zechariah! God has heard your prayer. Your wife, Elizabeth, will give you a son, and you are to name him John. You will have great joy and gladness, and many will rejoice at his birth, for he will be great in the eyes of the Lord. He must never touch wine or other alcoholic drinks. He will be filled with the Holy Spirit, even before his birth. And he will turn many Israelites to the Lord their God. He will be a man with the spirit and power of Elijah. He will prepare the people for the coming of the Lord. He will turn the hearts of the fathers to their children, and he will cause those who are rebellious to accept the wisdom of the godly."*[8]

That was a lot for Zechariah to take in! His wife, who had been barren, was going to give birth to a son in her old age. Their son would be filled with the Holy Spirit as well as have the spirit and power of the great prophet Elijah. And he would herald the arrival of the Messiah. Zechariah's son was the one the prophet Malachi had told them to expect! Zechariah had hoped and prayed all of his life for the coming of the Messiah, and I was telling him that his son would announce His arrival!

Zechariah asked, *"How can I be sure this will happen?"*[9] I expected Zechariah to be overwhelmed by my appearance and my message, but his doubt was not acceptable. It was obvious that I was an angel sent by God.

As a result of his lack of faith, God made him mute from that moment until after the birth of his son. His doubt prevented him for ten months from being able to loudly declare the good news that all of creation had awaited since the days of the Garden of Eden.

A little more than six months later, God sent me again. This time, I visited a young virgin in the village of Nazareth in Galilee. She was betrothed to a carpenter. *"Greetings, favored woman,"* I said to her. *"The Lord is with you!"*[11]

The young woman was startled by my appearance. She was also confused as to why I had called her "favored."

. . .

"Don't be afraid, Mary," I continued, *"for you have found favor with God! You will conceive and give birth to a son, and you will name Him Jesus. He will be very great and will be called the Son of the Most High. The Lord God will give Him the throne of His ancestor David. And He will reign over Israel forever; His Kingdom will never end!"*[12]

The young woman asked, *"But how can this happen? I am a virgin."*[13]

Unlike Zechariah, Mary was not doubting what I had said. She was most sincerely trying to understand how she could be with child.

I continued, *"The Holy Spirit will come upon you, and the power of the Most High will overshadow you. So the baby to be born will be holy, and He will be called the Son of God.*[14]

"What's more, your relative Elizabeth has become pregnant in her old age! People used to say she was barren, but she has conceived a son and is now in her sixth month. For the word of God will never fail."[15]

Mary's response was a testimony to the sovereignty of Almighty God. Of all of the young women God could have chosen to be the mother of His Son, He had chosen perfectly. "I am the Lord's servant," she responded. *"May everything you have said about me come true."*[16]

I didn't have long to wait before God sent me with His next message. I was to deliver it to the carpenter to whom Mary was engaged. He had just received some shocking news – she was with child – and he was not the father. His heart was broken. He loved this young woman. She had told him about my visit and he wanted to believe her. But Joseph feared God even more than he loved Mary. He could not continue an engagement that dishonored God.

. . .

So, that night I appeared to him through a dream. *"Joseph, son of David, do not be afraid to take Mary as your wife. For the Child within her was conceived by the Holy Spirit."*[17]

Once again, I witnessed the sovereignty of our Almighty God. When the carpenter arose, he did exactly as the Lord had commanded. He never questioned. He never faltered. He trusted God completely.

I would come to Joseph on two additional occasions: once to warn him of danger, and the second to let him know the danger had passed. Again, he would arise and obey. Jehovah God knew just the right man to entrust with the earthly upbringing of His one and only Son.

Almighty God gave me one more opportunity to announce the coming of His Son. This time it was to a group of shepherds on a hill overlooking the town of Bethlehem. The young virgin had just given birth to the Savior in a stable. And the Father intended for a small group of fathers and sons to come to the stable to worship His Son.

As I looked down on the shepherds to announce the birth of their Savior, I noticed one father and son in particular – Moshe and his son Shimon. They were initially fearful when I appeared. And when the angelic host joined me to proclaim, *"Glory to God in the highest"*[18] they stood frozen.

But I knew their hearts had received the message. I watched as they made their way to the stable. I watched as they bowed in worship. And again, I knew that Almighty God in His sovereignty knew exactly who needed to hear about the birth of His Son. He knew the ones whose hearts were prepared to hear and receive the good news. He knew the work He was doing that night in their hearts and lives. And He knew the work He would continue to do in the days and years ahead.

I may stand in the presence of God – but I am not omniscient or omnipresent. I am not an infinite being. I am a created being. I was created by God to bring the messages He told me to tell. Even as I brought the good news of the birth of His Son, I did not know what would follow in the days ahead.

Little did I know how He would be received. Little did I know what awaited Him. Little did I know the breadth and depth of the sacrifice He would make! But God was allowing even me to gain a greater understanding of the breadth and depth of His love …

∾

ZECHARIAH - THE PRIEST

I am Zechariah, a priest of the tribe of Levi from the line of Abijah and Aaron. The line of Abijah is one of the twenty-four priestly divisions established by King David. My father, Abdiel, was a priest, as was my older brother, Menachem. Our family lived and served in the hill country of Judea, in the city of Hebron.

Over four hundred years have passed since the writings of the prophet Malachi. The Persian Empire was defeated by Alexander the Great about one hundred years after Malachi died. As a result, Judea came under the rule of the Greeks. But later, the Greek civilization divided, and we became part of the Seleucid Empire. That is, until a priest named Judas Maccabeus led our people in revolt.

When Jerusalem was liberated, we enjoyed a brief respite of self-rule by the kings of the Hasmonean dynasty. Though we were independent, we were still influenced by the Seleucids. We enjoyed religious freedom, but our peaceful existence was precarious because of the competing empires surrounding us.

. . .

This was the political and religious condition at the time of my birth. In those days, our Hasmonean kings also served as our high priests; but otherwise, the priests of each division carried out duties as King David had decreed.

Five times each year our priestly division makes its way to Jerusalem to offer daily sacrifices in the temple and to convey priestly blessings. We serve two one-week periods each year, as well as during the three major feasts of Passover, Pentecost, and Tabernacles.

When I was a boy, barely a young man of fifteen who was still living in my parents' home, my older brother traveled to Jerusalem to serve for the second one-week course that year. He and I were close despite our age difference. I looked up to him and wanted to be just like him.

Even though he was still a young priest of only thirty years of age, the leading priests on that occasion granted him the opportunity to be one of the priests to enter into the holy place and present that day's offering of incense before the Lord. It was a once-in-a-lifetime opportunity that many priests never experienced, particularly one so young.

I prayed that one day Jehovah God in His mercy would grant me an opportunity to do the same. I was excitedly awaiting my brother's return home to hear all about his experience in the sanctuary. But he never returned home. He had died unexpectedly in his sleep. His young wife, my parents, and I were devastated.

Fourteen years later, I married a young woman named Elizabeth. She, too, is from the priestly family of Aaron and our parents have been close friends for many years. She was born around the same time my brother died, and our parents arranged our betrothal when she was still a child. Elizabeth and I earnestly prayed for a son. But as the years passed, we began to become painfully aware that God had other plans for us. Our hearts ached.

. . .

The world around us continued to change, as well. Ten years before I married Elizabeth, Judea became a client state of the Roman Empire. That meant we still had a Hasmonean king, but he now answered to Rome and our sense of independence was diminishing. But that, too, changed ten years after Elizabeth and I were married. The Roman senate installed Herod as the "King of the Jews" and established a more visible military presence throughout the region. There was no longer any illusion of independence. We were firmly under the control of Rome.

We were afraid that the pagan practices of our Roman conquerors would be thrust on us, but gratefully that did not happen. As a matter of fact, King Herod did something that soon caused him to gain our favor. He commissioned an extensive restoration of the temple. The First Temple built by King Solomon had been a majestic structure. But it was destroyed by our Babylonian captors.

The Second Temple reconstructed by Zerubbabel was a much more modest structure. Herod determined that a "great king" needed to make sure the people had a "great temple" in which to worship their God. The entire structure was completely refurbished. The restoration work was accomplished without any disruption to our worship or festival celebrations.

Each time I came to Jerusalem to carry out my duties as a priest throughout the construction period, I was amazed by the work that had been done. The work took about eight years to complete, and when it was finished the structure rivaled – and many would say eclipsed – the majesty and magnificence of the First Temple.

It's hard to believe that thirteen years have passed since the restoration was completed. I am now seventy-seven years old. Elizabeth is sixty-two and we long ago gave up on our hopes of becoming parents. We are well past the age of bearing and raising children.

. . .

Last week, I bid Elizabeth farewell and traveled from Hebron to Jerusalem to serve for the first one-week course of this year's service. It was a beautiful spring day. I will confess that the journey seemed less burdensome than usual. I had received word that I was to present the offering of incense on the altar in the sanctuary. I did not know which day I would be doing so, but I was one of the fourteen priests who had been chosen from my division for that week.

I couldn't help but think of my brother. Over sixty years had passed since he was chosen for this honor. I can remember his excitement – and mine for him. For a moment, my excitement turned to melancholy. I still missed him!

When I arrived at the temple, I learned I would present the offering at twilight on the first day of the week. I was grateful that I would not have to contain my excitement any longer.

As I entered into the temple's sanctuary, I was in awe. There before me was the veil that separated the sanctuary from the Holy of Holies. Only the High Priest is permitted to enter into the very presence of Jehovah God in the Holy of Holies – and that occurs only once per year on the Day of Atonement. I would never be closer to the Lord's presence than I was today.

I was quite emotional as I realized that no matter how righteous I endeavored to be, I was but a sinner standing in the presence of a Holy God. It was only by His mercy and grace that I was permitted to enter into this holy place to present this offering of incense to Him.

There before me, in front of the veil, stood the golden altar. The fragrance of incense permeated the air. First, I placed on the altar the burning coals I had brought from the bronze altar of sacrifice in the courtyard. Then, I prepared and placed the incense, made of equal portions of stacte, onycha, galbanum, and frankincense. As the sweet-smelling smoke of the incense rose as a pleasing aroma to God, I quietly prayed and interceded on behalf of the people.

Even though my eyes were closed, I suddenly sensed a light radiating before me. As I opened my eyes, I saw a man standing to the right of the incense altar. My first reaction was, "What is this man doing in here?" But quickly, I realized he was glowing. He did not appear to be the source of the light, rather he appeared to be reflecting a light. I knew this was no ordinary man. My heightened senses and emotions transitioned to fear. Why was this "man" here and what was taking place?

Suddenly, he spoke. *"Don't be afraid, Zechariah! God has heard your prayer. Your wife, Elizabeth, will give you a son, and you are to name him John."*[1]

He continued speaking – but honestly, I could not understand everything he was saying. He told me he was a messenger from God. Was he an angel? No one had heard a message from God in hundreds of years, and no one had seen an angel in longer than that. Did God still send angels, and did they speak to men? I am a sinner. How can I stand in his presence? What is he going to do to me?

Don't be afraid! Of course, I'm afraid! And he says Elizabeth will give me a son! How can that be? We long ago stopped praying for a son. Why is God answering now? We're too old! Is this a dream? Am I just hearing things? Surely, this can't be true!

I worked up the courage to ask, *"How can I be sure this will happen? I'm an old man now, and my wife is also well along in years."*[2]

To which he sternly responded, *"I am Gabriel! I stand in the very presence of God. It was He who sent me to bring you this good news! But now, since you didn't believe what I said, you will be silent and unable to speak until the child is born. For my words will certainly be fulfilled at the proper time."*[3]

. . .

My fear quickly melted into sorrow. God had sent one of His angels to bring me a message. He had waited until I was here in this special and holy place. At a time when my ears should have been the most attuned to the voice of my Lord, I had been fearful of His messenger. At a time when my heart should have been the most receptive to His message, I questioned if it were true.

Instead of rejoicing at this news, I had responded with disbelief. God was not only sending me a son – the son he was sending me would prepare the way for the arrival of my Messiah! And he would be filled *"with the spirit and power of Elijah."*[4]

The world needed to hear and know that the Messiah will soon arrive. For centuries we have waited to hear that good news. For centuries we have awaited the messenger who would come before Him. And now this angel has told me that the messenger was to be my son! But because of my faithlessness, I would be unable to proclaim the news.

I lifted my head to speak to the angel, but he was gone. The light no longer radiated in the sanctuary. I tried to speak, but no words came out; I was mute. I was unable to tell anyone, including my dear Elizabeth, this wonderful news. My heart was overjoyed – and heavy – all at the same time.

My service here in the sanctuary was complete. It was time for me to return to the outer court. But I didn't know how I would face those waiting for me. What should I do since I was unable to speak?

After a brief time, I came out of the sanctuary. One of my fellow priests was the first to approach me. He wanted to know what my experience was like. He was looking forward to one day presenting the offering of incense, too. But I couldn't answer him. All I could do was gesture.

. . .

He quickly realized I was unable to speak. Others began to gather around us. I heard one of the people say, "He is so overcome with emotion having presented the offering to Jehovah God that he can't speak." Some nodded their heads in agreement. Another said, "Perhaps God has given him a vision in the sanctuary!" Others said, "Zechariah, tell us what you saw!"

But I could not. And my muteness continued for the remainder of my week of service. After a while, my fellow priests just stopped asking. They looked at me with pity and told me everything would be all right.

It wasn't going to be all right – it was going to be great! The Messiah was coming … and so was my son! But I couldn't tell them that.

At the end of the week, I made my way back home. How was I going to explain this to Elizabeth?

Little did I know how or what I would say. Little did I fully comprehend the role my son would play. Little did I know how much more there would be to the story …

∾

MARY – THE VIRGIN

$\mathcal{J}$ am Mary, the Lord's servant, and I have truly been blessed.

I was born in the small town of Nazareth in southern Galilee. It is located in the hills a day's journey westward to the Mediterranean Sea and a day's journey eastward to the Sea of Galilee. About three hundred people live in our town, so everyone knows everyone else. It is an obscure town; there is no reason for anyone to come visit. There are no Roman palaces or bathhouses or paved streets. As a matter of fact, there are no Romans living here at all. All our residents are descendants of Abraham.

The town isn't very old. It was settled about sixty-five years ago when the Hasmonean rulers led our people to expand into the uninhabited regions of the wilderness. The surrounding land is fertile and produces plentiful crops of olives, grapes, and grain. My grandparents' family was one of the first to move here from Hebron. My grandfather, Matthat, was a carpenter and came here to help construct the cisterns, grain storage facilities, and olive and wine presses needed to support the crops.

My grandfather came from the tribe of Judah and the line of King David. My grandmother came from the priesthood line of Abijah and Aaron.

Their son, Eli, followed in his father's footsteps as a carpenter. He married a beautiful young woman by the name of Abigail. After four years of marriage, God blessed them with a baby girl – me!

My father did not have a son to teach his trade, but he had a daughter who loved to follow him around. I would sometimes hear my mother tell him to be careful that he did not spoil me. But she always did so with a smile and a twinkle in her eye. People tell me that I have my mother's gentle ways and my father's determination. But both of my parents continually reminded me that Jehovah God created me for His purpose, and they raised me to walk in His ways – no matter where He leads or how He leads.

My father often worked together with his friend Joseph, who also did not have a son. The two men were similar in age and manner. They were both kind and godly, and I could tell they greatly encouraged one another.

Their bond of friendship was never more obvious than when my mother unexpectantly died when I was nine years old. My father was overcome with grief. My parents had been deeply committed to one another as life partners and best friends. Though they both loved God first and foremost, they loved each other with all of their hearts. It was obvious that part of my father's heart died with my mother. I saw Joseph do everything he could to encourage my father – as did I.

I became the woman of the house. My grandmother was still living with us, and though she tried to help, she was elderly and limited in what she could do. I worked to maintain my father's home according to my mother's standards. And I tried to be strong for him.

Not long after my mother died, we received news that Joseph's wife, Rebekah, had also passed away. I watched as these two friends lifted each other up in their sorrow and encouraged each other in their continuing journey.

·   ·   ·

As the years passed, joy returned to both homes – and even, on occasion, laughter. On my fifteenth birthday, my father announced that he had offered my hand in marriage to Joseph. I was surprised he had done so without my knowledge. I always thought I would marry a man much closer to my own age. But Joseph was a kind man, and the idea of marrying him was not displeasing to me. I was more concerned about my father being left alone. Who would take care of him?

My father assured me that he would be fine, and he wanted to make certain that my future was assured. I had now reached an age where it was appropriate for this type of arrangement. But my father told me that Joseph had insisted he would marry me only if that is what I wanted. I promised my father I would pray and seek direction from Jehovah God.

It didn't take long before I had my answer. I told my father I would marry Joseph with a full heart. It was early December when my father publicly announced our betrothal. The marriage feast would take place in one year.

A few weeks later, I was walking alone in a nearby vineyard on a beautiful, cool day. I was thinking about all the changes the coming year would bring. I wondered what it would be like to be Joseph's wife. Suddenly, a man appeared out of nowhere in the path ahead of me. I was immediately struck by his appearance. A light was radiating off of him. Though it was a sunny day, his light was not from the sun.

"Greetings, favored woman!" he said. *"The Lord is with you!"*[1]

I looked around to see if anyone else was nearby. Nazareth was a small town, so I had never been concerned about going for walks in the fields by myself. But this man startled me. I knew everyone in town – and I did not know him! And he didn't speak like anyone I knew.

Obviously, he sensed my fear. *"Don't be afraid, Mary!"*[2]

· · ·

I asked myself how he knew my name.

"You have found favor with God! You will conceive and give birth to a son, and you will name Him Jesus. He will be called the Son of the Most High."[3]

As he spoke, a peace came over me, and I knew it was from the Spirit of God. It was the same peace God had given me about marrying Joseph. I knew that before me stood a messenger sent by God. Was he telling me that Joseph and I would one day have a child?

So, I asked the angel, *"How can this happen? I am a virgin."*[4]

He replied, *"The Holy Spirit will come upon you, and the power of the Most High will overshadow you. So the baby to be born will be holy, and He will be called the Son of God."*[5]

The Holy Spirit will come upon me! This will not be Joseph's child. He will be the Son of God! I was hearing the words, but I didn't fully comprehend their meaning. It was all so much to take in! A few moments ago, I was walking in a vineyard thinking about my future wedding – and now I was being told that I would bear the Son of God!

The angel closely watched my reaction before he continued. *"What's more, your relative Elizabeth has become pregnant in her old age! People used to say she was barren, but she has conceived a son and is now in her sixth month. For the word of God will never fail."*[6]

Elizabeth was pregnant! She is older than my father! This, too, is according to God's plan! And at that moment, I knew I needed to travel to Hebron to see her.

· · ·

"I am the Lord's servant," I said. *"May everything you have said about me come true."*[7]

Then the angel disappeared as suddenly as he had come. As I pondered our conversation, I knew I was not ready to tell my father this news – nor was I ready to tell Joseph.

I returned home and told my father that a messenger had just brought me word that Elizabeth was expecting a child and I needed to go see her. I didn't know how long I would be there, but I felt I needed to go assist her. My father was so overjoyed for Elizabeth and Zechariah that he never inquired about the messenger. He encouraged me to go with his full blessing.

My father knew of a group of merchants who were preparing to leave for Hebron the following morning. The journey would take about a week. Gratefully, Jehovah God in His sovereignty had already prepared a way for me to make the journey, so I departed the next morning.

As I traveled to Hebron, I kept thinking about how I was going to tell my father ... and Joseph. And now, how was I going to tell Elizabeth? Would she believe me when I told her about an angel appearing to me? And would she believe what he had said?

When I arrived at their home, Zechariah was gone. But Elizabeth greeted me. Immediately I saw that she was great with child. And she had the glow of an expectant mother. I was so happy for her.

But I was taken aback when she cried out to me saying, *"God has blessed you above all women, and your child is blessed. Why am I so honored, that the mother of my Lord should visit me?"*[8]

· · ·

I didn't need to worry about what I would say to Elizabeth – she already knew! She continued, *"When I heard your greeting, the baby in my womb jumped for joy. You are blessed because you believed that the Lord would do what He said."*[9]

I had only been carrying the Son of God for a few days. There was no physical sign that I was pregnant. I had told no one about the angel or what he had said. But Elizabeth knew it all. I doubted that everyone I encountered in the days ahead would know the truth before I told them. And I was sure that not everyone I told in the future would believe me. But for that moment, Elizabeth and I embraced, knowing that God was going before us and He had indeed blessed us greatly!

After we settled in her home, I proceeded to tell her about my encounter with the angel and what he had said. She then told me about Zechariah's encounter with the angel in the sanctuary of the temple. The angel said their son would be called John and he would prepare the way for the child in my womb. And then she told me the angel's name was Gabriel.

"Gabriel," I said, "a messenger from Almighty God! Thank you for telling me his name."

I stayed with Elizabeth and Zechariah for three months. I tried to help her as much as I could for those last three months of her pregnancy. We rejoiced together throughout that time and knew that God had given us those weeks together.

It was now early April. I was beginning to show – ever so slightly – that I was carrying a child. And I knew I must return to my father and Joseph before it became more obvious. I received word that another caravan was preparing to make its way back toward Nazareth and I knew the time for my departure had arrived.

·   ·   ·

It was obvious that the arrival of Elizabeth's baby was drawing near, but we also knew that I could not delay my return home. So, Elizabeth and I embraced as we said farewell.

All the way home, I continued to ask Jehovah God how He would have me tell my father and Joseph. I knew He would show me. He would not abandon me.

When I arrived home, my father and Joseph were together in my father's house. They both warmly greeted me and anxiously received my news about Elizabeth, Zechariah, and the baby they were expecting. I told them how the angel Gabriel had come to Zechariah in the sanctuary of the temple.

They told me they had seen Zechariah in the temple over Passover and how they had discovered he was mute. Now they understood why!

I told them what the angel had said and who the baby was to become – the messenger preparing the way for the One who would also soon arrive. They rejoiced in the news, not only for Zechariah and Elizabeth, but for all mankind. They were hearing the announcement we had hoped to hear all of our lives!

And then I told them about the day Gabriel had appeared to me before I left for Hebron and what he had said. I shared how Elizabeth had greeted me when I arrived in Hebron. I told them what had transpired over the past three months. And I announced that I was carrying the child within me. The Holy Spirit had come upon me and the baby in my womb was now about three months along.

Their excitement about Elizabeth's news now turned to shock. I was not receiving the same reaction from either one of them that I had received from Elizabeth. I could see they were both trying hard to understand. But they sat there in silence, not even asking a question.

. . .

As I came to the end of my account, I said,

> *"Oh, how my soul praises the Lord.*
> *How my spirit rejoices in God my Savior!*
> *For He took notice of His lowly servant girl,*
> *and from now on all generations will call me blessed.*
> *For the Mighty One is holy,*
> *and He has done great things for me.*
> *He has helped His servant Israel*
> *and remembered to be merciful.*
> *For He made this promise to our ancestors,*
> *to Abraham and His children forever."*[10]

My father and Joseph looked at each other and then at me. Neither spoke a word. Both got up and walked out of our home, leaving me to stand there alone. As they went outside, they silently walked off in different directions. I turned to my Heavenly Father and prayed.

Little did I know how they would respond. Little did I know how others would respond. Little did I know what the Father had in store for His Son in my womb. But I knew I could trust Him. And I knew I would trust Him ...

~

ELIZABETH – THE COUSIN

I am Elizabeth, the wife of Zechariah, and I am a blessed woman.

My father was a priest from the ancestral line of Zadok, a descendant of Phineas, the son of Eleazar, the son of Aaron. Zadok was chosen to serve as the high priest of Israel by King David and continued to serve in that capacity throughout the reign of King Solomon. He was the first high priest to serve in the First Temple in Jerusalem.

Zadok's descendants continued to serve as high priests in the temple even through the Babylonian exile. My ancestor, Ezra, was sent to Jerusalem by King Artaxerxes to serve as the Zadokite high priest in the newly restored Second Temple. And his descendants continued to serve in that capacity until they were pushed out by the Hasmoneans about one hundred fifty years ago.

For centuries, our Zadokite priestly line preserved the Messianic prophecies of Isaiah and the foretelling that the Messiah will come from the line of King David. The Hasmoneans, however, desired to usurp the legitimate royal line of King David by making themselves the kings of Israel. That is what motivated them to also seize the legitimate priestly role of my ancestral family. We currently live in a socio-political environment that is hostile toward anyone claiming that the Messiah will come from the line of David.

As a result, my father and other Zadokite priests believed the activity in the temple and the actions of our Sanhedrin were more politically motivated than spiritually motivated. They saw that many of the teachings and actions of our religious leaders were attempts to manipulate truth for their advantage rather than advocate adherence to absolute truth.

That prompted a number of our Zadokite priests to form a sect within Judaism called the Essenes. Not only do the Essenes believe the Messiah will come from the line of David, they also devote themselves to charity and benevolence, studying the books of the elders, preservation of truth, prayer, and fellowship with one another.

While I was still living under my parents' roof, my older brother left Hebron to go raise his family in Qumran among the Essene adherents. By that time, my family had already made marriage arrangements for me to be wed to Zechariah. So, Hebron would continue to be my home.

From a young age, I sought to honor God and to obey all of His commandments. I tried to live righteously and circumspectly before the people around me. Hebron had been one of the cities given to the patriarch Caleb, and it had been one of the initial cities of refuge. I desired to be a reflection of the faithfulness exemplified by Caleb and his family – and for my home to always be a place of refuge.

Zechariah and I were married when I was fourteen years of age. He was twenty-nine, and he was handsome. But more importantly, he was a good man and a godly man. Though I can't say that I loved him when we were first married, I grew to love him. Actually, we grew to love each other. And I am thankful to Jehovah God for the husband He has given me.

· · ·

My hope and prayer, even before we were married, was that God would grant Zechariah and me a home filled with sons and daughters. Zechariah had often quoted a psalm of Solomon: *"Children are a gift from the Lord; they are a reward from Him."*[1] My prayer was that God would greatly reward my husband! But as the years passed and I was unable to conceive, it appeared God had different plans for us.

Honestly, though, the desire for children never left my heart. Even as I approached the age where motherhood was no longer an option, my longing still persisted.

Zechariah traveled to Jerusalem about a year ago to perform his priestly duties in the temple for the eighth week of the new year. He was particularly excited about this trip. He had been chosen to burn the offering of incense on the altar in the sanctuary. He had prayed for that opportunity all of his life, and now at the age of seventy-seven his prayer was being answered. I was excited for him as I watched him leave and begin his journey.

Zechariah traveled to Jerusalem for one week five times a year. Sometimes, I would join him. In recent years, rooms had been added to the temple complex to provide lodging for the visiting priests and their wives. My widowed sister-in-law, Anna, now lived in one of those apartments year-round, so I occasionally joined Zechariah in order to visit her – as well as participate in the celebrations in the temple. This time however, I stayed home.

The week Zechariah was gone went by quickly. It was springtime and I was busy preparing and planting our small field for what I hoped would be a bountiful harvest of fruits and vegetables. As a matter of fact, I was in the field when Zechariah returned home.

I saw him approaching from a distance. I was surprised he was not calling out to me like he usually did. I expected him to run toward me, excitedly sharing about his time in the sanctuary. But he seemed unusually subdued.

As he gave me his customary embrace, he was completely silent.

"Has the cat got your tongue?" I teased. "Why are you so quiet? Tell me all of your news! I want to hear all about your time!"

But I knew something was wrong when I saw the sadness in his eyes. He began to gesture and it quickly became clear that he was unable to speak. Somehow, he had become mute! He kept pointing toward heaven, and then he would place his hand on my stomach. Next, he made a gesture as if he were cradling a baby in his arms.

As the afternoon wore on, we continued in our attempt to communicate. He made gestures and wrote some words in the dirt and then on a tablet. I also asked him questions that he could answer with a nod of his head. Finally, I was able to piece together the story.

An angel named Gabriel had appeared to him while he was in the sanctuary. He told Zechariah that we were going to have a son and his name would be John. And he would prepare the way for the coming Messiah!

No wonder Zechariah was silent – that was a lot to take in! But he helped me understand that God had made him mute because of his initial reaction of disbelief. I was grateful to learn that his condition was temporary, and his speech would return after our son was born.

That night I marveled at all of this news! I had stopped hoping for a child. I was sixty-two years old, and I was soon to be a mother. Our prayers were being answered. The kindness of the Lord was overwhelming. *"He has taken away my disgrace of having no children,"*[(2)] I exclaimed.

. . .

It wasn't long before I became pregnant. My excitement grew each day – along with the baby in my womb. But it was challenging to explain to people what was happening – particularly in light of Zechariah's muteness. We finally decided it would be easier if I remained secluded in our home. So, for the next five months I had little contact with anyone.

One afternoon during the sixth month of my pregnancy, a young woman approached our home and called out to me from the entry. When I went to greet her, I realized it was my young cousin, Mary, from Nazareth. (My father's sister had married a man from Nazareth by the name of Matthat. Mary was their granddaughter.)

But then the most amazing thing happened. When Mary spoke to me, the baby within me leapt. I felt the flush of a presence come over me. I was filled with knowledge that had no explanation other than the Holy Spirit had just come upon me.

As I looked at Mary, I immediately knew that she, too, was with child. Though she was not showing yet, my spirit just knew she was carrying a child. And this was not just any child. This child was the Son of the living God. The child she was carrying was the very One for whom my son was being sent to prepare the way!

"God has blessed you above all women, Mary," I exclaimed, "and your Child is blessed."(3) As I ushered Mary into my home I said, "Why am I so honored, that the mother of my Lord should visit me? When I heard your greeting, the baby in my womb jumped for joy."(4)

Mary explained how an angel had appeared to her, and how he had told her she would conceive a child as a virgin and give birth to a son. And the child would be the Son of the Most High.

. . .

I asked her to describe the angel's appearance. Her description was identical to what I had been able to glean from Zechariah. I could not contain my excitement as I explained to her what the angel Gabriel had told Zechariah.

Mary interrupted me and said, "The angel told me, *'Your relative Elizabeth has become pregnant in her old age! People used to say she was barren, but she conceived a son and is now in her sixth month. For the word of God will never fail.'"*[(5)]

I do not know who was more encouraged at that moment – Mary or me! Though neither of us had any real doubt leading up to that moment, that conversation was such a precious confirmation. Mary bore witness to what Zechariah had heard, and Zechariah's account bore witness to what Mary had heard.

We were walking through an experience together that no one else could fully understand – one that had never occurred before and never would again. Yes, we both were women blessed to be bearing a child – but these were not just any children. Mary's was the Son of the living God, and mine was the messenger who would prepare His way. All of creation was awaiting their arrival. All of time was pointing to their birth. And here they were in our wombs!

I looked at Mary and said, *"You are blessed because you believed that the Lord would do what He said."*[(6)]

Mary stayed with me for three months. It gave us the opportunity to talk about many things. She told me that she was betrothed to a carpenter. She had not yet told him about the angel's visit or the child she was carrying. She feared how he would react. He was a gentle man and a God-fearing man. Would he understand? What would he do? She hadn't yet told her father, either. She had come straight away to see me.

·   ·   ·

I reminded her that the same Holy Spirit who had come over me to tell me about the child she was carrying before she uttered a word was able to speak to her father and Joseph. The same God who enabled a barren old woman and a virgin to each conceive a child was able to do all that was necessary to prepare their hearts to receive the news. Again, I said, "You are blessed because you believed … and so will they."

Mary soon returned home, and the time arrived for my baby to be born. Most of my neighbors had not known I was pregnant, so when they heard I had a son, they rejoiced that God had been merciful to me.

When my baby was eight days old, all of our neighbors came for the circumcision ceremony. They kept suggesting that we name him Zechariah in honor of his father. But I exclaimed, *"No! His name is John!"*[8]

They responded, *"But there is no one in all of your family by that name."*[9]

They sought to gain Zechariah's approval of their suggestion. He motioned for a writing tablet, and to everyone's surprise wrote, *"His name is John."*[10]

Then instantly, my husband's voice returned, and he began to praise God! Zechariah told all of those gathered about the angel who had appeared to him and what the angel said. The entire community was in awe as the news spread throughout the Judean hills. *"What will this child turn out to be?"* they exclaimed. *"Because the hand of the Lord is surely upon him in a special way!"*[11]

God has blessed us with this precious son in our advanced years. We know that God has all things in hand. We asked Him to show us to whom we should entrust our son if we are to die before he is grown. The Lord reminded us that He has already prepared my brother's son, Adriel, who lives in Qumran to raise our son when that day arrives. He has given us a peace that nothing in our son's life has been left to chance.

. . .

As Zechariah said,

> *"Because of God's tender mercy,*
> *the morning light from heaven is about to break upon us,*
> *to give light to those who sit in darkness and in the shadow of death,*
> *and to guide us to the path of peace."*[12]

Little did I know how that morning light would break or exactly what the path of peace would look like, but I know who does. And I will trust Him …

∾

ELI – THE FATHER

*M*y name is Eli, and I am the son of Matthat of the line of King David from the tribe of Judah. I am a carpenter in the town of Nazareth. I learned my trade working alongside my father, just as he learned working alongside his father.

As a carpenter, I build the storage buildings and presses needed to process the crops produced in the hills surrounding our home. I exploit the soft limestone of the region to build storage basements for the oil and wine pressed from our olive and grape harvests. I am quite adept in excavating and crafting our structures using the natural limestone available.

My father and I had almost finished excavating a storage basement in the base of a hill on the south side of town. My father was inside the basement doing some of the finishing work when the ceiling collapsed. The basement was immediately filled with falling rock and debris … and my mother instantly became a widow.

I was an only child so I became the patriarch of our family that day – assuming responsibility for my mother. Then, about one year later, I married a young woman by the name of Abigail. There was no question she stole my heart from the moment I first saw her. Her name means "gives joy" – and joy certainly returned to our home the day she and I wed.

With the death of my father, I needed to find a fellow carpenter with whom I could partner. A carpenter named Joseph had recently arrived in our town. He had moved here from nearby Cana because he had heard work was available. He seemed like an able fellow, so I approached him about working together.

He and his wife, Rebekah, became good friends to Abigail and me. We had similar natures. We shared a passion for God and a desire to serve Him wholeheartedly. When Abigail and I learned that we were expecting a child, they were the first people we told. We knew their hearts rejoiced with us – even though we also knew they longed to have children of their own.

Our little Mary entered into this world about eight months later. From the day she was born, she was a precious gift to her mother and me. I looked forward to the end of each workday so I could be home with my girls – my wife, my mother, and now my daughter. I regretted that my father had never known little Mary – he would have been as besotted with her as I was.

By the time she was four, she would plead with me to bring her along to work. She told me she wanted to be a carpenter just like me. Gratefully, Abigail was there to nurture Mary into becoming a proper little girl. But Abigail would still often lovingly warn me not to spoil Mary. Though she always did so with a smile, I knew there was good counsel in those words.

As Mary grew, she demonstrated a deep-seated and sincere love for Jehovah God. I couldn't imagine a happier life than we were enjoying.

·   ·   ·

However, one day that happiness was shattered when my precious Abigail died. Joseph and I were working on the north side of town when Rebekah brought me the news that Abigail had fallen ill, and I was needed at home. Abigail was already dead by the time I arrived. There had been no warning and no indication she was sick. God had suddenly taken her home.

My greatest comfort through those difficult days was my nine-year-old daughter. Though we tried to comfort one another, I knew she did a better job of comforting me than I did of her. In many respects, it caused her to quickly mature beyond her years. Despite my attempts to allow her to still be a child, she became the young "woman" of the house – caring for both me and my mother.

Joseph was also a great strength to me as I walked through those difficult days. Sadly, it wasn't long after that I was called on to be his strength. Rebekah fell ill with a fever that could not be abated, and one week later she died. Mary and I did the best we could to comfort Joseph, but with our own loss being so recent, we mostly just grieved together.

When Mary was twelve, my mother died. It was another season of sorrow that we walked through together. But just before she died, my mother had challenged me that one day soon I needed to make arrangements for Mary to be wed. She encouraged me to pray and ask Jehovah God to show me what He would have me do. And that is what I did for the next couple of years.

One day, Joseph and I were again working together as we often did. Somehow our conversation steered toward a discussion of whether either one of us would ever marry again. As he spoke, I sensed a longing in his heart.

Later that night after we parted company, I began to wonder if he and Mary would be a good match. There was a great age difference between them. He was just a few years younger than I was! But he was a kind man

– gentle, hardworking, and godly. I knew I would never find a man of any age whom I could trust more to care for my daughter, to love her, and to provide for her. And Mary had become far more mature than her years.

I continued to ponder and pray about the possibility for several months. Then late one afternoon, I approached Joseph with the idea. I wanted to talk to him first and see if he was agreeable before I talked to Mary. I would not force any marriage on her. I just wanted God's best for her.

Joseph was taken by surprise when I approached him. "Surely you can find a much better match for Mary," he said. "Someone who is closer in age with whom she can live a long and happy life."

"I believe I know you as well as I know any man," I responded. "We have walked together through sorrow and joy. We have worked together, and we have played together. Most importantly, we have prayed together. I have seen your heart – and you have the heart of a man I want for my daughter. And you have the heart that my daughter wants in a husband. Don't give me an answer now. Pray to Jehovah God and consider what He would have you do. And then we will talk again."

He agreed to do so. Several days later, he came back to me with his answer. He would marry her – but only if Mary was certain she wanted to marry him. He would not enter into any marriage agreement if she had reservations.

So, I set off to speak with Mary. I was surprised by her reaction. The concerns she expressed were mostly her apprehension about leaving me alone. The idea of marriage to Joseph was not displeasing to her. I told her that Joseph wanted to be certain that she didn't have any reservations. As I expected, she told me she would pray and seek direction from Jehovah God.

. . .

Within a matter of days, she gave me her answer and in early December I proudly announced the betrothal of my daughter to Joseph the carpenter. We had agreed the marriage feast would take place on the same day the following December. Our neighbors all extended their well-wishes and Mary, Joseph, and I were joyful that God was ordering our steps.

About a month later, Mary told me that a messenger had delivered the news that our cousin Elizabeth was expecting a child. Elizabeth is quite a bit older than I am. She and her husband, Zechariah, were both in their old age – and they had no children. So, this was quite a miracle! Mary told me she needed to go to Hebron to be of help to her. I knew the companionship would be a blessing to Elizabeth – and I also knew it would be good for Mary.

Earlier that day, I had encountered a group of merchants who were departing for Hebron the next day. It appeared that Jehovah God had already made the arrangements for Mary to make the trip! She departed the next morning.

I will confess that my home was very empty for the next three months. I missed Mary. Her absence left a great void in our home. But I also knew it was good preparation for me for the future.

The Passover Feast was approaching, so Joseph and I made plans to go to Jerusalem together. Passover is always a good opportunity to catch up with family members we don't regularly see. It is a great occasion for thankfulness to Jehovah God and celebration with family.

When we arrived at the temple, I sought out my cousin Zechariah to find out how Elizabeth and Mary were doing. I knew he would be pressed by his priestly responsibilities, but I was confident we could find a moment to speak. However, when I did catch up with him, I was alarmed to discover that he was mute.

. . .

He communicated with me through gestures and a few words written quickly on a tablet he carried for that purpose. He conveyed that he and Elizabeth were overjoyed to be expecting a son. I rejoiced with him over the news. He expressed their gratitude for Mary's visit, and the great help and companionship she was providing to Elizabeth.

It seemed his muteness had something to do with his time in the sanctuary – but I couldn't fully understand what he was trying to tell me. I was confident Mary would fill me in on the details when she returned home. He indicated that he needed to proceed to the sacrificial altar, so we hastily said our farewells.

Later that day, Joseph introduced me to his cousin Achim, and his wife, Miriam. They lived nearby in Bethlehem. Joseph delightedly told them about his engagement to my daughter and that he looked forward to introducing her to them next Passover. Good wishes were expressed all around before we went our separate ways. Our time in Jerusalem went by quickly and we soon returned to Nazareth – and to my empty home.

A few weeks later, Mary returned! Joseph was there with me in our home and we were both overjoyed! My home lit up when she arrived!

Immediately she told us the news from Hebron, including Zechariah's encounter with an angel. We could not contain our excitement over the news about the coming Messiah or the role Zechariah and Elizabeth's son would play in preparing the way. God had truly blessed them! And with the announcement about the Messiah, He had truly blessed all of us!

But then, Mary's story took a surprising turn. Apparently, she, too, had been visited by an angel – here in Nazareth – the day before she left for Hebron. She had waited three months to tell me what He said. And she was now bearing a child – the Son of the Most High God. The Holy Spirit had "come upon her." What exactly did that mean? The Messiah, whose arrival we were all anticipating, was inside the womb of my daughter! And she hadn't told me!

. . .

It was a lot to take in. I looked at Joseph and he looked at me. We both looked at Mary. I didn't know how to respond. I needed to compose my thoughts and pray. I decided the best thing I could do was get alone with God. I was flooded with emotion. And I did not want emotion to control what I said. So, I did the only thing I knew to do – I walked out of the house. I noticed Joseph was right behind me, but I didn't want to talk to Joseph. I wanted to talk to God.

I know I hurt Mary by abruptly walking out, but I didn't know what else to do. I made my way to the vineyard to walk and talk with God.

In the vineyard, a peace came over me. First, I knew Mary. And I knew everything she ever told me was true. I knew that if she told me, then an angel had come to her. If she was pregnant, then the Spirit of God had come upon her! As I thought about how a virgin could conceive a child, I was immediately reminded of the words of the prophet Isaiah:

> "Behold, the virgin shall conceive and bear a Son,
> and shall call His name Immanuel."[1]

Nothing was too difficult for God. And by His grace, He had selected my daughter – Abigail's daughter – to be the mother of His Son!

Why had she waited to tell me? I could only imagine how this news had overwhelmed her. This was a lot for a fifteen-year-old to take in! And she had done so with grace. Then wisely, she had gone to see Elizabeth to seek confirmation.

The momentary hurt I felt because she had kept this news from me faded away and was replaced with great pride. Pride in who my daughter had become, and pride that God thought even more highly of my daughter than I did.

. . .

With that, I ran back home and embraced Mary.

I knew the road ahead would be difficult for her – but for now I just wanted to rejoice with her! And I wanted her to know that I loved her!

Little did I know how Joseph would respond. Little did I know how our friends and neighbors would respond. Little did I know what it would mean to be the mother of the Son of the Most High God! But I knew that the One who had so ordered her steps would continue to do so ...

∾

JOSEPH – THE CARPENTER

I am a carpenter named Joseph. My father, Jacob, was a carpenter, as was his father, Matthan. As a matter of fact, my ancestors have been carpenters as far back as anyone can remember. Well, maybe not as far back as *anyone* remembers. My ancestor David was actually a shepherd – until he became the King of Israel. And his son Solomon is considered by many to have been the wisest king our people ever had.

Thirteen of my ancestors, who were the successive descendants of Solomon, followed him in ruling over our nation as kings of Judah. Most of those did evil in the eyes of the Lord – so I share my family connection to them with great reluctance. But there is no denying that royal blood courses through my veins.

We are God's chosen people living in the land that He promised our patriarch, Abraham, about two thousand years ago. He brought us into this land through the leadership of Moses and Joshua fourteen hundred years ago. But though we dwell in the land God gave us, we have been living here as conquered captives for over five hundred years. Our people have been subjected to foreign rule – first the Babylonians, then the Persians, the Greeks, the Seleucids, and now the Romans.

. . .

When you stop to think about it, we have been captives in our own land longer than we were foreigners and slaves in Egypt. We have long grown weary under the rule of our pagan oppressors who have little to no regard for our Lord God Jehovah. We pray for deliverance from our oppression much like our ancestors prayed for their deliverance from Egyptian bondage.

Through the prophets, our God promised to send His Messiah to deliver us. Each generation for hundreds of years has hoped and believed He would come in their lifetime. But four hundred years have passed since the last great prophet, Malachi – and all we have heard from heaven is silence! Our hearts are heavy and our hope has grown dim, but we live our lives trusting our God for His promise.

Since King David grew up in and around the town of Bethlehem, it is considered to be my ancestral home. Some of my relatives still live there. But over the centuries, much of my family has scattered to other parts of Judea and Galilee. My great-great-grandfather, Eliud, led his family to settle in the city of Cana. The town had been destroyed by the Assyrians many years before, but Eliud and others came to rebuild the town. His carpentry skills were put to great use as the town rose from its ashes. And the following generations assisted in continuing that effort. My younger brother, Clopas, and I made a steady living there with our carpentry skills.

But work began to slow down in Cana, and I heard there was more opportunity in nearby Nazareth. My brother, Clopas, was reluctant to make the move, so I encouraged him to remain in Cana while my wife, Rebekah, and I relocated.

Soon after arriving in Nazareth, I met a carpenter named Eli. He needed a co-laborer and I needed steady work – so we agreed that Jehovah God had brought us together. Eli, and his wife, Abigail, soon became good friends with Rebekah and me.

. . .

I remember the day Abigail gave birth to a baby girl they named Mary. She was the apple of Eli's eye and he doted on her from the day she was born. Eli would occasionally bring her to work with him when she was a little girl. I watched her grow from a tiny infant into a tender young woman. She had a soft and gentle nature. She honored her parents in all that she did and exhibited a great love and reverence for our God. She was a hard worker and demonstrated a quick wit.

Abigail died when Mary was nine, but I will never forget the tenderness she showed her father as he walked through his grief – despite the fact that she was walking through her own.

Then, not long afterward, my Rebekah died. She had developed a high fever that the rabbi and midwives were unable to cure. Eli and Mary were a great comfort to me during my time of grief.

Rebekah and I were married for twenty years. We had not been married long before we realized Rebekah could not have children. It caused us great sadness throughout our marriage – but we knew it was the will of God. Still, I regretted not having a son to mentor. A few years after Rebekah's death, I started wondering, and praying, if God would give me an opportunity to marry again and give me a son. But I never expected how God would answer that prayer!

Eli and I watched as Mary continued to mature into a radiant young woman. She caught the attention of many young men in our town. So, no one was more surprised than I when Eli approached me about marrying his daughter. Since I am only slightly younger than Eli, I am old enough to be Mary's father. Though such an age difference is not uncommon in marriages of our day, it still was not a match I had considered. However, I admit the possibility was captivating. I told Eli that I would pray about his offer.

Over the next several days I made a rather lengthy mental list of the reasons why I was not the right man for Mary. But I could not think of one single reason why she would be unsuitable for me. As I prayed, I sensed God was leading me to go back to Eli.

"I would be honored and humbled to take your daughter Mary as my wife," I told Eli. "I would care for her. I would provide for her. And I would love her with my whole heart. But before I can give you an answer, I must know that this is what Mary wants, as well. I will not enter into a marriage arrangement that she does not want. So, you need to discuss the matter with her and let me know what she says."

Truth be told, I thought it would be the last time he and I ever spoke of it. I was certain Mary had her heart set on a different match. I was shocked when he returned a week later to tell me Mary was also in favor of the match. She desired to become my wife! It was all I could do to keep from shouting with glee – and thanking God for His goodness! Of all men, I was the most envied when three weeks later we announced our betrothal. We set a date for the wedding feast to be held one year from the day of our betrothal.

I continued to be the happiest – and most blessed – of men as I awaited the consummation of our marriage. Soon after our announcement, Mary unexpectedly traveled to Hebron to visit her cousin for three months. When she returned, she came to Eli and me with startling news. She told us she was pregnant! But she assured us she was still a virgin. She told us that she had become pregnant by the Holy Spirit.

"An angel by the name of Gabriel appeared to me," she said. "He told me that God has decided to bless me! He said I would become pregnant and have a son. He will be very great, and He will be called the Son of the Most High God. The Lord God will give Him the throne of David. And He will reign over Israel forever. His kingdom will never end.[1]

"I asked the angel how this could be possible," she continued, "and he told me that the Holy Spirit would come upon me, and the power of the Most High God would overshadow me."

. . .

Mary then turned her attention to me. "Joseph, I have not broken our vows. This is an act of our Most High God. I do not fully understand what is happening – but I know I must trust Him. And I need to know that you trust me. Do you trust that all I have told you is true?"

My heart was broken! I hadn't really heard everything she said after she told me she was pregnant. She said something about the Holy Spirit coming upon her. But all I could think about was this young woman, whom I thought was without guile, had somehow sullied herself and broken our contract. I thought about the shame and disgrace to come for her and my friend, Eli – and the hushed conversations that would happen behind my back.

Without saying a word, Eli got up from his seat and walked out of his home. I did the same. My heart was full, and at that moment I could not speak. As I made my way back home, I kept going over what she had said. I had gone from being the happiest of men to feeling like a broken one.

But as much as I hurt, my love for her did not diminish in any way. I decided the right thing to do was quietly break our betrothal so as not to disgrace her publicly. Eli could then send her away to stay with a distant relative.

My sleep that night was fitful. But in the midst of it, an angel of the Lord appeared to me in a dream. In it he said, *"Joseph, son of David, do not be afraid to go ahead with your marriage to Mary. For the child within her has been conceived by the Holy Spirit. And she will have a son, and you are to name Him Jesus, for He will save His people from their sins. All of this has happened to fulfill the Lord's message through His prophet:*

Look! The virgin will conceive a child.
She will give birth to a son, and He will be called Immanuel
(meaning God is with us)."[2]

When I awoke the next morning, I ran to Eli's home. Both Eli and Mary wept as I told them what the angel had said. "Mary, I trust that all you have told me is the truth," I said. "I trust you and I trust God. How favored you are above all women! And how favored am I to become your husband and a father to this One who is in your womb!"

I was delighted to learn that God had led Eli to the same realization. Though we rejoiced in the news, we also knew what people in our town would say. Mary, most of all, would be ridiculed and falsely accused of improper behavior. We trusted that God would give her – and all of us – the strength we needed to endure. Mary came home with me that day to be my wife, but she remained a virgin until after the baby was born.

We were right! Most of our neighbors kept their distance from us, with the exception of a young neighbor girl named Salome. She was a constant source of encouragement and companionship for Mary. But most of those we told about the angel's visits looked at us with suspicion. Others looked at us – particularly Mary – with disdain. I hated that for her. God by His grace had chosen her to be His vessel. She was to be honored, not despised. But life was never going to be the same. There would always be whispered inuendoes.

For centuries our people had awaited the arrival of the promised Messiah. I had always hoped He would come during my lifetime and that I might get a glimpse of Him. But in my wildest dreams I never thought my wife would give birth to Him. I had prayed for a son – and God by His grace had chosen me to be the earthly father of *His* Son.

All I could think about was how inadequate I was to be His father and Mary's husband. But I knew the same God who could enable a virgin to give birth to His Son would empower a lowly carpenter to be the father and husband He needed me to be. By His grace, I would trust and follow Him!

· · ·

A few months later, we received word that the Roman ruler, Caesar Augustus, had decreed that a census be taken throughout our land. We were all to return to our ancestral homes to be registered. I made preparations for Mary and me to make the three-day journey to Bethlehem.

The baby would soon be born. This was not a good time for a trip. But we didn't have a choice. Once again, I admired Mary's bravery – not only for making such a trip during this stage of her pregnancy, but also because of the stares and whispers she would endure.

Eli had planned to travel with us since he, too, was of the line of David. But two days before we were to leave, he came down with a fever. The rabbi and midwife had seen this fever before. They treated him with an elixir made from herbs and bark. They assured Mary and me that he would recover, but he did not have the strength to travel to Bethlehem. We would go on without him and one of the midwives would look in on him in our absence.

I planned for us to stay at the home of my cousin Achim in Bethlehem. I hoped he would welcome us with open arms. Shortly before our departure, I received word from my brother Clopas that he, his wife, and their young son would be joining us for the journey. We were grateful that we would have their companionship as we traveled. They would, however, be lodging with his wife's sister when they arrived in Bethlehem.

So, we set off on our journey to our ancestral home – the town of David.

Little did I know where all the journey would lead …

~

JACOB – THE ELDER

J am Jacob, the leading elder and rabbi in Nazareth. My father, Joazar, was sent from Jerusalem to this town by the Hasmonean high priest John Hyrcanus II to serve as the first leading elder of our town. Nazareth was one of the towns being established by the Hasmoneans in the uninhabited wilderness. People were relocating here from other parts of Galilee in the quest to establish a new life in a land of greater opportunity.

Those coming were primarily uneducated farmers, vineyard workers, animal herders, and tradesmen. A local synagogue was the first building established in the center of our town and it was my father's job to oversee its formation.

I was born soon after my parents arrived in Nazareth. While I was still a boy, my father took me to Jerusalem to be educated at the feet of the Sadducean rabbis. For a short while, I was also schooled under the teaching of the sage Hillel who became well-known for his statement: *"That which is hateful to you, do not do to your fellow. That is the whole Torah, the rest is the explanation; now go and learn."*

. . .

My father raised me to be a Sadducee. Though the Sanhedrin in Jerusalem includes both Pharisees and Sadducees, the latter have enjoyed the favor of the Hasmoneans, as well as the Romans, because we esteem power and control over the finer details of doctrine. I share my father's belief that power and prestige are definitely preferred over piety.

My education focused on the tenets of the law of Moses in a similar way to the Pharisees but dismissed the idea of our own immortality. I was raised to believe that there is no resurrection of the dead either for punishment or reward. Our actions, like our souls, stop at the grave. That means our actions today yield their own reward, and money and power are the most desirous of those rewards.

I soon understood that the law can be leveraged in a very convenient way to gain even greater power and control. I studied diligently and modeled the behaviors I witnessed in my father and my teachers. It equipped me for my return to Nazareth to follow my father as the lead elder.

While in Jerusalem, I also experienced the disdain that people in Judea held for Galileans. The people of Galilee were considered uneducated, unsophisticated, and ordinary. When I told people I was born in Nazareth, many asked, "Can any good thing come out of Nazareth?" I soon learned to say my family came from Jerusalem. That statement received greater respect no matter where I was in Judea or Galilee.

As a matter of fact, my father arranged my marriage to the daughter of a Sadducean leader in Jerusalem in order to further build up my social pedigree. I knew from a young age that everything was about outward appearance – and that includes our religious practices. Do not give an offering without making sure that others see you give. Do not pray if others cannot hear you. Do not help someone unless you know they can do something for you in return.

Nazareth is a small town, so it is fairly easy to stay abreast of all the news. I am in the most powerful role in our town. I am fully aware that knowledge is power, so I work to stay informed under the guise of my spiritual leadership of the people. My role as rabbi and elder gives me the ability to use that knowledge to lead our people to think and act in a way that best suits me.

Eli the carpenter lives in our town. His father, Matthat, arrived in Nazareth at the same time as my father. He was one of the main craftsmen responsible for building our synagogue. Matthat was a skilled worker, known for his kindness and humility. The same is true of Eli.

Eli's now deceased wife bore him a daughter named Mary. She was a pleasant girl who showed great strength of character and compassion as she grew. As I watched Mary come of age, I knew she would be a much sought-after prize for our eligible young men. So, I was surprised last year when Eli announced her betrothal to Joseph the carpenter. The day of the wedding feast was set for one year later.

Joseph is about the same age as Eli and also a widower – his wife died soon after Eli's wife. I knew that Eli and Joseph were good friends, but I never expected Eli to select Joseph to be his daughter's husband. And I was not alone. I overheard several conversations at the synagogue about that very subject. Between Joseph's age and his limited prospects, many of Eli's neighbors thought he could have done much better in selecting a husband for his daughter.

A few weeks after the betrothal was announced, Mary left Nazareth. It was all arranged very quickly. We heard she was going to visit her cousin. Eli arranged for her to join a caravan of merchants traveling to Hebron. He told me Mary was going to provide a helping hand to her elderly cousin who was expecting her first child.

Three months later, Mary returned home. Two days after that, Joseph took her to be his wife. We were all surprised, but if that is what they decided to do, we would accept it.

. . .

But we soon discovered that Mary was with child – and the midwife told me she was a little more than three months along in her pregnancy. That meant she was either pregnant just before leaving for Hebron or soon after arriving there. So that left people wondering whether Joseph and Mary had consummated their marriage before they took their vows – or if Mary had engaged in an adulterous act.

As the lead elder and rabbi of our town, it was my responsibility to find out which was the case. I sent word to Eli, Joseph, and Mary to come meet with me in the synagogue. When they arrived, Eli spoke first. "Rabbi, thank you for inviting us to come speak with you. We have planned to do so, but events have unfolded quickly. We want you and all of our neighbors to rejoice with us in our good news. So, please allow us to tell you what has occurred. Mary will speak first."

But before Mary could speak, I said, "It is my duty to know what has transpired so the reputation of this synagogue and our citizens is in no way sullied. I have been told that Mary is more than three months pregnant, so events have not unfolded all *that* quickly. I need to determine if anything has occurred that dishonors God or this community. If anything untoward has happened, we will then discuss appropriate action. Mary, I caution you to be certain that you speak the truth."

"The day before I departed for Hebron," Mary began, "I was out walking alone in the vineyard when I was approached by one whom I now know to be an angel of the Lord named Gabriel. He told me, *'You have found favor with God! You will conceive and give birth to a son. The Lord God will give Him the throne of His ancestor David. The Holy Spirit will come upon you, and the power of the Most High will overshadow you. The baby will be holy and He will be the Son of God.'*"[1]

She then went on to tell me how the angel told her about her cousin becoming pregnant and relayed the story of how this same angel had spoken to the priest Zechariah. The angel said the priest's son would be a messenger preparing the way for the baby in Mary's womb.

· · ·

Joseph confirmed that he and Mary have not consummated their marriage. She is – and will remain – a virgin until after the baby is born. Then he told me how this same angel had come to him in a dream. The angel told him the child in Mary's womb had been conceived by the Holy Spirit. Joseph was not to be fearful about proceeding with his marriage to Mary. All of this was to fulfill the prophecy of the prophet Isaiah, *"The virgin will conceive a Child."*[2]

Then Eli spoke up and told me how God had given him a peace that his daughter was to be the mother of the Messiah! "This is joyous news!" he said. "The Messiah for whom we have all waited for centuries will soon arrive! Yes, He is even here with us right now – in the womb of my daughter!"

They all looked at me with an exuberant joy on their faces. They were obviously expecting me to join in their celebration! And what's more, I think they expected me to assemble the entire town to rejoice in their news!

But nothing could have been further from my mind! "I directed you to tell me the truth," I said, "and all you have told me are these wild stories! You tell me of an angel coming to you, Mary, in a vineyard, and you, Joseph, in a dream. Who are you that an angel of God would come to you? Angels have not walked on this earth for hundreds of years, but you expect me to believe that one has come no less than three times, including to the old priest in the temple! If he had entered the temple, he would have appeared to the High Priest. If he had come to Nazareth, he would have appeared to me. He would not have come to uneducated people such as yourselves!

"Your story is preposterous! How could a virgin conceive a child? Either you all are naïve or have been bewitched by this girl! Or perhaps, Joseph, you decided not to wait for the year as announced but decided to consummate the marriage sooner. And if so, that is your prerogative if you and Eli have come to that agreement. But don't make up this wild story to cover up your impatience!

. . .

"And do not attempt to justify your story by tying it to a questionable prophecy from Isaiah. You know our Hasmonean leaders dispute the veracity of his prophecies, and they deny the belief that the Messiah will be a descendant of David. You have used statements that no one believes to try and justify your lie! How dare you dishonor God and dishonor me by saying these things! This is blasphemy!"

"We have told you the truth!" Eli countered. "The Spirit of God will confirm that truth to you if you seek Him in prayer – just as we have done!"

I could no longer control my anger. "How dare you speak to God's anointed in that way!" I shouted. "Joseph has said he and Mary have not consummated this marriage. Either he is lying, or Mary has committed adultery with another man. The idea that the Spirit of God has come upon her is preposterous! There are no witnesses to indicate that she has committed adultery. I can only conclude that the two of you have had relations – as is your right – and the baby is a product of that act.

"I will not allow you to tell your outrageous story to the people of this town! If you do, I will denounce it as heresy and call into question whether Mary is an adulteress who deserves to be stoned to death. Otherwise, we will let the people believe that you have terminated your one-year betrothal period and consummated your marriage. There will be no wedding feast!"

I then got up and walked out of the room. As I did, I shook my robes to reflect my disdain for their actions and their words. As they watched me leave, I saw their hurt and disbelief.

In the days that followed, whenever I encountered anyone speaking in hushed tones about Mary, Joseph, or the child in her womb, I would simply look down piously and shake my head. My displeasure and disapproval were obvious from my response – and I would never breathe a word of any of the heresy they had uttered to me. Most people kept them at a distance for the weeks and months that followed.

Several months later, Caesar Augustus announced that a census was to be taken. Everyone was to return to their ancestral hometown to be counted. Nazareth was not anyone's ancestral hometown, so everyone would be leaving for the census. When it came time, there were a few people who were either too weak or too ill to travel. They remained in town, together with our midwives who would care for them. Eli was one of those who was sick. I couldn't help but wonder if God was punishing him for his part in the deception.

As I watched Joseph and Mary leaving to make their way to Bethlehem, I again thought about what they had told me. Surely it was all lies. God wouldn't choose to send His Messiah through a nobody from Nazareth of all places! Would He?

Little did I know the truth. And little was I wanting to know the truth. I would go to my grave with my heart closed off to the truth ...

$\sim$

ACHIM – THE HOST

*M*y name is Achim. My family and I live here in Bethlehem, the town of our ancestor David, the shepherd king. Our town is situated in the midst of rolling green hills, which produce some of the best almonds and olives throughout the province. The soil is fertile because we sit on top of an enormous aquifer. As a matter of fact, our water is known as the best tasting around. The story goes that some of King David's mighty men risked their lives by crossing through Philistine lines to get him a cup of this very water.

Bethlehem was once one of the fortress towns established by King David's grandson, Rehoboam. It was a defensive military installation designed to safeguard the water source, which also supplied Jerusalem and other surrounding villages. But now under Roman rule, it is less of a fortress and more of a sleepy village secluded from the noise and activity of Jerusalem.

The hills in and around Bethlehem are ideal for raising sheep. Our rich soil and plentiful water provide an abundant food supply. The demand for lambs in Jerusalem continues to grow. They are the principal animal sacrifice offered in the temple throughout the year.

· · ·

And during the feasting days, Jerusalem is filled with pilgrims from all over the land who aren't able to bring their own animals to sacrifice. The pilgrims rely on the lambs and birds that are available at the temple. That creates great demand – and profit – for local shepherds.

However, I am not a shepherd. Like many others in my family, I am a carpenter. There's not a lot of work for carpenters in Bethlehem, but there is in Jerusalem. It is a bustling city with new structures and dwellings being added every day. Since we live close to Jerusalem, I can work there but still be at home most nights, sleeping in my own bed and enjoying my wife's good cooking.

My wife, Miriam, and I have three grown sons, all of whom work with me. They are good sons who never gave us cause for concern. They each married self-respecting young women who grew up right here in Bethlehem. And now Jehovah God has blessed them all with children – which means Miriam and I have been blessed with many grandchildren. My ancestor King Solomon once wrote that *"children are a gift from the Lord"* and *"happy is the man whose quiver is full of them."*[1] And God continues to give me a bigger quiver!

But not only is our quiver getting bigger – so is our home! Each time one of our sons married or had more children, we added another room. Like most of the homes around here, ours is made of stone with wood timber beams to support the upper floors. Our home abuts a hill, so the stable for our animals is actually a cave that I enlarged within the hill.

Since our family has continued to grow, we added a third level to our house a few years ago. The center courtyard is open to allow for cooking, eating, and gathering. That is where we spend most of our time together. The other rooms either surround or overlook the courtyard. These rooms provide adequate space for sleeping and privacy. I intentionally added extra rooms to allow space for our guests. And if our family keeps expanding, we will add even more rooms!

· · ·

Caesar Augustus recently decreed that a census be taken and everyone must return to their ancestral home for that purpose. Our extended family has scattered across the provinces, so we have been anticipating the arrival of a large influx of distant and not-so-distant relatives. We will be expected to host them and provide them with lodging.

I am grateful that we – as well as our other extended family members who also live here in Bethlehem – are able to accommodate all of them. Miriam and our daughters-in-law have been busily making preparations. And as the patriarch of our extended family here in town, I have made sure that the other families are doing the same.

I was really looking forward to seeing my cousin Joseph. Though we live some distance apart, we still see each other from time to time. He is just a few years younger than I am and we have much in common. When I last saw him in Jerusalem for the observance of Passover, he told me that he was betrothed to a young girl from his village.

Miriam and I were so glad to hear it. There has been too much sadness in his life with the death of his wife Rebekah. The marriage feast for him and his bride was planned for later in the year, so I did not expect her to be traveling with him. Even though they are betrothed, I was certain she would be traveling with her family for the census.

But this afternoon, Joseph arrived at my door with a young woman. And not only was she with him, but she was great with child! Miriam immediately came scurrying to the doorway to greet the girl.

"You are radiant, my dear," Miriam exclaimed, "and you must be weary from your journey." Then she made a move to embrace the young woman – until I reached out to stop her. She and I looked at each other disapprovingly.

. . .

"Achim and Miriam," Joseph spoke up, "this is Mary, my wife." Miriam and I looked at Joseph, then at Mary – followed by a not so subtle stare at her obvious "baby bump." The silence became awkward. I didn't know what to say, and Miriam knew, based on my actions, that she should not say anything.

Joseph again broke the silence and said, "I know you must have questions. But may we come in so Mary can be seated, and we will explain what all has occurred?"

Miriam nodded her head and reached out a hand to help the young woman step across our threshold. But I continued to block the doorway and removed Miriam's hand from the girl's shoulder.

"Yes, I do have questions, Joseph," I said. "And they must be answered before you can enter my home. When is the child she is carrying due?"

"Any day now," Joseph replied. He obviously knew what I was about to ask.

"When I last saw you," I continued, "you told me that you were betrothed to this young woman and the marriage feast was still nine months away. That was only a little more than six months ago. How can she now be expecting a baby any day, and how is it that she has become your wife in advance of your wedding feast?"

Joseph responded by telling us the most preposterous story I have ever heard. He said Mary had been visited by an angel who told her that the Spirit of God would come upon her and she would give birth to His Son. Then the angel had subsequently appeared to Joseph and told him the same thing. So, he had gone ahead and formalized their marriage contract right then and brought her into his home. He assured me, however, that she was still a virgin.

· · ·

Either she was a liar and he was so lovestruck that he was blinded to her deception – or they were both liars and had made up this unbelievable story to cover up her adultery. If the baby was his, why had he told me in Jerusalem they had not yet consummated their marriage? Whoever heard of Jehovah God coming upon any woman to give birth to a baby?

Babies are only conceived one way – and it takes a woman and a man! And whoever heard of angels appearing to anyone? Of course, there were stories in Scripture about how angels appeared to the patriarchs, but that was a long time ago. That doesn't happen anymore!

I began to seethe with rage. This was most obviously a violation of God's commandments and I could not accept it. I could not welcome them into my home because I would be lending credence to this outrageous story and violating everything I believed to be righteous and holy. Joseph was my relative, and in many respects had become my dear friend. And yet, here they stood as an abomination before God – expecting to enter my home as if everything was all right.

In my anger, I told them there was no room for them in my home or in the homes of any of our family members. I even went on to say that I would see to it they were not welcome in any home in Bethlehem – there was no room for them! They had sinned against God and they had stained our family name. Then I turned my back to them and said, "Go away from my home!"

Before I turned my back, I saw the deep hurt in their eyes. And I saw a resignation that confirmed this was not the first time they had been treated this way. They looked sad, but I saw no anger. Perhaps they were expecting a different reaction from family – maybe compassion or acceptance. After all, darkness was drawing near and I was turning away a pregnant woman, who was about to give birth at any moment. And they were family. But my beliefs would not permit me to compromise.

. . .

Just then Miriam spoke up. "You can spend the night in our stable. It will provide shelter, and the animals will provide warmth from the cool night air. There is straw to provide you with a comfortable resting place, and I will bring you food and water for the night."

Mid-sentence I had turned toward Miriam to silence her, but she stared back at me with a look that left no doubt it was my turn to be silent.

"Thank you for your kindness," said the young girl. Then the two of them silently walked to the stable.

At that moment, I regretted what I had said and done. But I couldn't compromise my convictions – and I just could not believe their story. Nonetheless, I was now grateful that Miriam had spoken up. However, she didn't speak to me for the rest of the night. She just gazed at me with cold eyes. And I knew there was nothing I could say right then that would make things better.

Other distant family members arrived that night and we welcomed them into our home with open arms. We didn't tell them – or even our sons and daughters-in-law – about Joseph and Mary staying in the stable. Other than the silence between Miriam and me, we acted as if everything was normal. But there wasn't a moment that passed that I didn't think about the couple in the stable.

Little did I know what would occur that very night ...

MOSHE – THE SHEPHERD

I am a shepherd named Moshe. I have watched over sheep in these Bethlehem hills since I was a young boy. My father and grandfather were both shepherds as were their fathers and grandfathers – all the way back to the shepherd king himself, David. He knew these hills like the back of his hand, just like each of us has ever since.

There was a time during the captivity of our people in Babylon when my ancestors were not shepherding in these hills. But by the grace of Jehovah, He made the way for us to return many years ago.

There is nothing else I would rather be doing, and there is nowhere else I would rather be. Jehovah God has blessed me greatly. He is the greatest Shepherd of all! He has chosen us to be His people – His flock, if you will. He watches over us and cares for us. He provides for us and leads us where He wants us to go. He teaches us to know His voice. And He has given us His commands to protect us.

He has blessed me with a loving and beautiful wife. I will unashamedly admit that I do not deserve her. She is a gift from God. Her name is Ayda, which means "joy." And there is no denying that she has brought joy into my life. One way is through the birth of our five children – three boys and two girls. I will probably spoil my daughters – at least that is what Ayda tells me – but I will teach my sons how to be good shepherds, just as my father taught me. As a matter of fact, my oldest son Shimon, who recently turned ten, is already a great help to me. Though he looks just like me, he has his mother's quick wit and her gentle spirit.

Ayda gave birth to our youngest son just three nights ago! We named him Eliezer, which means "gift of God." All of our children are a gift, but Ayda bore him with great difficulty. We were not sure he would survive, but by God's grace He did. His precious life truly is a gift. Shimon and I were watching over the flock when my oldest daughter Hannah came running into the hills to tell us of his birth. It was a glorious night – filled with joy, excitement, and thanksgiving.

Excitement is palpable throughout our town. Not because Eliezer was born, but because our sleepy little town is filling up with visitors. The Roman emperor decreed that a census be taken, and everyone is required to return to their ancestral home. I am grateful I didn't need to travel to get to my ancestral home – I already live here! And my family never scattered to other places, so Ayda and I were not expecting any guests for the census.

Honestly, with Ayda just giving birth, we were grateful that we weren't expecting company. But many of our neighbors were anticipating and preparing for the arrival of extended family from other towns. There are many unfamiliar faces in town. Whoever thought a government census could bring this much excitement!

Last night, Shimon and I were back in the fields watching over our sheep. As usual, other shepherds were also on the hillside watching their flocks. It was a clear still night without a cloud in the sky. The sheep were contented, so it was a quiet night in the hills. And as we looked down on the town, it, too, was still.

. . .

Apparently, people were resting after a busy day of visiting and making preparations. Shimon was excitedly telling me how he and his younger brother Jacob were going to help me train up Eliezer to be a good shepherd. I swelled with pride as I listened, realizing what a fine young man my son was becoming.

Suddenly, our tranquility was interrupted by the appearance of what looked to be a man – but a man unlike any I have ever seen. He was surrounded by a blinding light. While I raised a hand to shield my eyes, I instinctively reached out to pull Shimon close to my side. I squinted at the other shepherds who were near. We all were trying to discern what was happening and what we should do.

Did this man mean us harm? Should we run? But we all knew we could not abandon our sheep! Who was this man and what did he want? I quickly realized the light was drawing me in. Instead of feeling threatened, the light seemed to embrace us. Don't misunderstand – we were afraid! But at the same time, we were spellbound.

It seemed like an eternity before the man spoke. *"Don't be afraid! I bring you good news of great joy for everyone! The Savior – yes, the Messiah, the Lord – has been born tonight in Bethlehem, the city of David! And this is how you will recognize Him: you will find a baby lying in a manger, wrapped snugly in strips of cloth!"*[1]

We were still trying to understand who this being was when, all of a sudden, the sky was filled with a heavenly host. As if in unison, we all fell to our knees in fear and shielded our eyes from the brilliance that radiated above us. At that point, we knew this was a host of angels – the army of heaven – who had come to bring us great news. The angelic host began praising God, saying:

> *"Glory to God in the highest heaven,*
> *And peace on earth to all whom God favors!"*[2]

As the angels proclaimed this news, time seemed to stop. Even the sheep surrounding us seemed to bow low. No one – and no thing – was capable of moving. We were overwhelmed by the sight and enraptured by the news. I have no idea how long the angelic host remained in our midst. But it was a sight and a sound that were forever imprinted on our memories.

Then, just as quickly as that host appeared, they were gone. For a few moments, our gaze remained fixed on the heavens. Gradually, we looked at one another and almost in unison said, *"Come on, let's go into Bethlehem! Let's see this wonderful thing that has happened, which the Lord has told us about."*[3]

Then we did something that shepherds never do! We left our flocks unattended in the field. We didn't stop to secure our sheep in the sheepfold. We didn't hesitate for one moment. We ran into town to the stable where the angels had directed us.

I realized the stable belonged to the carpenter Achim. It was a cave carved out of rock in the side of the hill. As we approached, we expected to find a large crowd gathered to worship the arrival of the newborn Messiah. We thought the religious leaders would be gathered to give praise to God – and perhaps even King Herod himself would be there. This was a great night of rejoicing for our entire nation in celebration and worship. Glory to God in the highest!

But we were dumbfounded when we arrived at the stable and no one was there. Not even Achim and his family were gathered. Only the baby's mother and father – and a few animals – gathered around the baby wrapped in strips of cloth laid in a feeding trough. Surely this wasn't the place! Surely this wasn't the baby! And yet, we knew it was! Where was everyone? Why weren't the streets filled with celebration? Why were we seemingly the only ones who knew Who this was?

As we entered the stable, we startled the man and woman. I am sure they wondered why these men were invading their private moment with their newborn. The baby's mother wasn't much older than Ayda when she and I married. Neither she nor the man, who appeared much older but we assumed was her husband, spoke one word to refuse us entry. It was as if they were expecting our arrival.

Shimon was the first to step toward the baby to get a better view. He looked up at the baby's mother for permission, and she smiled and nodded her head. The baby's father did the same. As I gazed at these parents, I realized their expressions were the same Ayda and I had just three nights earlier when Eliezer was born. I don't think we would have been as welcoming to strangers, but this couple was inviting us to join them in this very personal moment of love, thanksgiving, and blessing.

Yet, the other shepherds and I sensed there was something more. We were entering into an atmosphere of worship and adoration in that stable. Even the animals seemed to sense it. We told the couple about the angelic host. We told them what had been said and why we had come. Neither responded. Instead, the mother gave us a tender smile and, with a knowing look, nodded her head. Immediately, each of us fell to our knees and worshipped the baby lying in the manger.

Again, time seemed to stand still. None of us wanted this moment to end. Our hearts were so full we couldn't utter a word. And the reality of all we had heard and were now seeing became clear. The Messiah that the Lord God Jehovah had promised through the prophets of old had now come. The message of His arrival had been delivered to us – a group of shepherds on a hillside.

The Messiah, whom generations had anticipated, was now lying there before us in an animal's feeding trough. God had made the announcement through His angels to us! He hadn't made it to the religious leaders or the king, He had made it to us! He had entrusted the good news of the angelic message to a group of shepherds!

. . .

I looked at the baby's mother and realized she was tired. She needed her rest. Quietly, we stood to our feet and reverently backed out of the stable. Shimon was the last to get up. I could see that he was staring into the baby's eyes. As I looked closer, I saw that the little boy's eyes were dark brown, just like Shimon's.

But His eyes had a unique quality, particularly for an infant. His eyes were inviting and gentle. They welcomed you in and made you feel safe. But they also seemed to look into your very soul. Even though newborns are not able to focus, this one appeared to do just that! Shimon remained there, seemingly locked in a gaze with the baby. After a few moments, I softly called to Shimon to join me.

We had a lively discussion about what we had seen, heard, and experienced as we made our way back to the fields. Our conversation was so animated that a few passersby stopped to ask what was happening. We explained what we had seen and what the angel had told us.

Though they seemed amazed by our report, none was interested enough to seek out the newborn baby. Maybe the thought of angels announcing the arrival of the Messiah to a group of shepherds was just too hard for them to believe. But we knew the truth, and it would remain in our hearts forever!

This morning, my son ran to the stable to check on the baby and his parents. But no one was there. We hadn't thought to ask the family's names or where they were from. They had probably come to Bethlehem for the census. And though Shimon asked some people nearby, no one knew that a family had even been there. All that remained in the stable was the manger where the baby had lain, the animals that had surrounded Him, and the memory of a holy moment.

Little did I know the impact that baby's life would have in the days and years to come on me ... my family ... our town ... and on a world that hadn't been prepared to welcome Him.

MIRIAM – THE HOSTESS

I am Miriam and have lived my entire life here in Bethlehem. In ancient times, the town was called Ephrath, meaning "fruitful." The first reference to Ephrath in our history is that Jacob's wife, Rachel, died near here giving birth to their youngest son, Benjamin. That is significant to me because my lineage follows the tribe of Benjamin. As a matter of fact, King Saul was one of my ancestors. My lineage follows his oldest daughter, Merab.

You may recall that King Saul offered to give Merab in marriage to David if he would fight the Philistines. David declined the offer, but subsequently married Saul's younger daughter Michal. My husband, Achim, comes from the line of David. We often joke that if David had married Merab instead of Michal, Achim and I would have probably been related. But instead, I remained a Benjamite, while Achim's lineage followed the tribe of Judah.

Achim and I have known one another since we were children. Our families made an agreement while we were both still very young, so it came as no surprise when we wed one another. I couldn't have been happier! I had always admired Achim. He is an honorable man – always seeking to do the right thing. If he has any fault, it is that once he makes up his mind, there is no changing it. His decision is final.

I have always respected his decisiveness and been grateful that he is a man of integrity. He fears God and seeks to honor the commandments without fail. He instilled those same traits in our sons. Achim and I have had disagreements on minor things, just like most married couples, but for all of our thirty-five years of marriage we have been like-minded when it pertains to God's law. That's what has made this week so hard.

My daughters-in-law and I had been busy for weeks making preparations for out-of-town family members who would be staying with us for the census. We were looking forward to reuniting with family we hadn't seen for some time. One of those was Achim's cousin Joseph. He and his wife, Rebekah, had visited with us once years ago. We were sad for him when we learned she had died.

Then when we saw him in Jerusalem at Passover, we were overjoyed to hear he was betrothed. Happiness had returned to his life. And if anyone deserved some happiness, it was Joseph. So, we were looking forward to his visit and celebrating his good fortune with him while he was here in our home.

When Joseph arrived at our doorway earlier this week, Achim excitedly called out for me to come join him in welcoming our special guest. But I was surprised when my husband did not extend a warm and enthusiastic greeting. Quite the contrary, he appeared to be distressed.

I could see a beautiful, young woman was with Joseph. She was obviously pregnant. She had that radiance that all expectant mothers have. I could see she was exhausted, so I wanted to quickly get her in our home and off her feet. I wasn't even thinking about who she was or why she was with Joseph.

· · ·

I just saw an expectant young mother who needed to rest. My maternal instincts had taken over as I reached out to escort her into our home. But I was confused when Achim stopped me. I could not imagine why he was being so inhospitable. That simply wasn't like him.

Obviously, Joseph and the young woman saw our disagreement and felt uncomfortable during the awkward silence that followed. Joseph was the first to speak. "Achim and Miriam, this is Mary, my wife," he said.

Immediately my mind started to race. When we saw Joseph in the spring they had only just been betrothed. He had said the marriage feast would be this coming December. But she was now obviously nine months pregnant! I looked at Joseph, then I looked at the young woman, and then I looked at Achim. The puzzled expression on my face must have been obvious. I didn't know what to say!

Joseph asked if they could enter so Mary could sit down and rest, and he would provide us with further explanation. That made perfect sense to me. We had to let this poor woman get off her feet, so again I reached out to help her inside. I couldn't understand why Achim continued to stand in the doorway and block their entry, but I was particularly put off when he removed my hand from Mary's shoulder. Achim was determined to continue the conversation at the doorway and not allow this couple to come inside.

Achim confronted Joseph with the obvious question. Joseph then told us about the Spirit of God, an angel, and a statement that Mary was still a virgin! I will confess it all sounded pretty outlandish!

I could tell Achim was getting angry – and I understood why. Achim believed that, at best, his cousin and this young woman had broken their marriage covenant and Joseph had lied about it. Or, at worst, this young woman had broken the seventh commandment that states, "*Do not commit adultery.*"[1] And Joseph was trying to cover up her sin.

. . .

Regardless, they had sinned against God and Achim could not ignore their sin. They were guilty before God. And for my husband, if he allowed them into his home, he would be condoning their sin. His beliefs would not allow him to do that! Therefore, he did the only thing he knew to do – he told them there was no room for them in his home. He even told them there would be no room for them in any home in Bethlehem.

I saw the sadness and hurt in the couple's eyes. I saw the exhaustion on Mary's face. And I saw the concern Joseph had for his pregnant wife. At that moment, I was overcome with compassion. No, I didn't believe their story, but I also was not going to turn my back on this young woman who needed someone to give her shelter. It didn't matter whether Joseph was our relation or not – I would not turn away any mother in that condition!

So, I did something I had never done. I openly contradicted my husband. I ignored what he said and told them they could spend the night in our stable. Achim started to interrupt me – but I gave him a look that said I was not going to back down on this.

I directed the couple to the stable and told them I would bring them food and water for the night. I told Achim that we would not breathe a word of this to anyone, including our family. Achim would usher any guests into our home and stable their animals himself. No one was to have contact with Joseph and Mary. My husband and I did not exchange another word that evening.

Later that night after everyone was asleep, I heard the faint cry of a baby. I knew the sound was coming from our stable. I wanted to go see if the couple needed anything, but I decided against it. I did not want to bring attention to them by stirring – and I did not want to further upset my husband.

A short time later, I heard a commotion out in the street. Everyone was asleep in our town. Who would be making such a noise at this time of night? I quietly got up from my bed and looked out the window. It was a group of shepherds. I could see they had made their way to the stable. I had no idea what they were doing there – and now I had to see for myself. It was one thing to not tell anyone about our guests in the stable, but it was quite another to allow them to come to any harm.

I slipped outside and peered into the stable. I couldn't believe what I was seeing. I recognized the shepherd Moshe and his young son. They, and the rest of the shepherds, were kneeling on the straw before the baby in the manger – praising God and worshipping the infant. I heard them tell Joseph and Mary how angels had appeared to them in the fields telling them about the child's birth. The angels had said the baby is the Messiah – and I could tell the shepherds believed every word they were repeating. Maybe Joseph's story was not as far-fetched as we thought!

The shepherds remained there for some time as a holy hush came over that place. I saw Moshe's son linger before the baby as the rest of the shepherds began to leave. Then I looked at the faces of Joseph and Mary. There was a tenderness and even a worshipfulness in their eyes. There wasn't any shame! Something unusual – and perhaps unexplainable in our own minds – was taking place. I decided I needed to return to the house and tell Achim what I had witnessed.

To his credit, he never questioned whether what I was saying was correct; he just listened as I relayed the events. I told him we needed to invite the family into our home. Whether what I had heard was true or not, we could not allow this young mother and newborn to sleep outside in the cold.

There was no convincing Achim that the baby was the Son of God or that Mary was a virgin. But he agreed that she and the baby could come into our home and stay until Mary's time of purification came. He was resolute, however, that Joseph could not join them. He would have to leave. As a matter of fact, he would not be permitted to remain in the stable.

· · ·

Mary and the baby were to stay in the room on the upper floor. None of the family would know they were there, and they would not be permitted to have any contact with anyone else in our home. I realized there would be no further discussion with Achim on these matters. These arrangements would have to do.

The two of us went out to the stable to tell Joseph and Mary. I helped Mary bring the baby inside and got them settled back down for the night. I was grateful that the baby did not cry and awaken anyone. Throughout the weeks that followed, I was amazed at how quiet the baby actually was.

Achim spoke with Joseph and they agreed that he would go to Jerusalem. He could find carpentry work there for a few weeks. He would register for the census early in the morning and then be gone. He would return in eight days for the baby's circumcision, but otherwise he would stay away until it was time for him and his family to return home.

Early every morning and late each night I brought Mary food and water. For the first few days, Mary rested and regained her strength. And each morning I lingered just a little bit longer in her room. The baby was beautiful with dark hair and dark eyes. In fact, He had the most compelling eyes I had ever seen. When I looked into them, I believed they were intently looking right back at me. I knew that none of my sons was able to do that as babies. But there was something different about this child!

One night, my granddaughter Sarah surprised me by following me to the room and discovering our secret. To her credit, she never told anyone else, including Achim, about Mary and the baby. I was actually grateful for the added help to care for our guests, and I think Mary was glad for the companionship of someone closer to her own age.

As the days and weeks passed, I continued to mull over all that was happening. Were the shepherds right? Did they hear correctly? Was Joseph speaking the truth to us? Is this really the Son of God sleeping in our upper room? Is this truly the Messiah we have been awaiting? Surely, He couldn't be. Would God send His Messiah in such an unusual way? As each day passed, the more I began to believe it was true.

Little did I know what was still to come ...

~

BALTHAZAR – THE SCHOLAR

y name is Balthazar and I am a lifelong student of the science of the stars. I grew up and live in the city of Babylon. Once the center of the greatest empire on the face of the earth, it is now a provincial capital in the somewhat lesser Parthian Empire. The empire encompasses the whole of the Levant along the Mediterranean Sea, excluding the city of Tyre.

Our province includes all of the region that makes up the Tigris-Euphrates Valley. The Silk Road trade route between the Roman Empire and the Han dynasty of China passes through our province, making us a prosperous center of trade and commerce.

My father was the governor of our province, paying proper tribute to and supplying soldiers to our king. Because of this arrangement, our king is often referred to as the "king of kings." I am my father's second son, so he did not groom me to become the next governor. Rather, I have been permitted to pursue my love of science and have become one of the leading magi of my province.

. . .

I have enjoyed a life of privilege and was educated in the palace by some of the finest scholars in the world. Over the years, our empire has adopted the art, architecture, cultures, and religious beliefs of the ancient Babylonians, the Greeks, and the Persians. And now, through our commerce, our beliefs and culture are also influenced by the Romans and the Chinese.

I was just a boy when I became intrigued by the patterns between the movement of the stars and the earthly events they affected: for example, the rising and falling of tides as well as the changes in the seasons. The Persians predicted events based on the movement of stars, too – but events such as the rise and fall of kingdoms, the foretelling of the births and deaths of rulers, and the like.

During King Darius's rule of Persia, he sought a Hebrew wise man named Daniel to give him counsel. Daniel employed many of the Hebrew writings, as well as some of his own, to help interpret coming events. Some of those writings pointed to a coming King who would become the King of all kings.

For generations, first the Persians and then the Parthians studied the stars to determine when this King would be born. One of my teachers was preoccupied with this study. He ignited that same passion in my heart. So, I have dedicated my days and nights for decades, watching the stars in anticipation of their announcement of this King's birth.

And then that singular event occurred! About a year ago, a new uncharted star arose in the eastern sky. It was brighter than any other ever recorded. Travelers from China confirmed that my fellow magi in their country had also identified this star as a new celestial phenomenon; they, too, had begun to chart it. The discovery appeared to coincide with the Hebrew writings that a special king would one day be born. He would not be just any king – He would be the "King of kings." And the star had appeared in order to lead us to Him!

. . .

I had prepared for this moment my entire life! My older brother was now our ruling governor, so I asked for his approval to undertake a royal expedition to follow the star and convey our good wishes to this King. It was agreed that I would bring Him a gift worthy of such a King. We decided the gift would be a weight of highly fragrant frankincense. It comes from the trees in the valley of our province and is the finest in the land.

My young servant, Yanzu, also was becoming one of my best pupils. I decided he would join me on the expedition, and I gave him charge over the chest containing the frankincense.

Preparations were made within a matter of days. My protégé, two of my servants, including Yanzu, and I set out on our camels. The star was leading us to the west – but in order to avoid the pitfalls of traveling through the Arabian desert, we headed northward toward the sea, along the bank of the Euphrates River.

We had been traveling for several days when we came upon another caravan of travelers who were also following the star. I learned that they were actually two caravans that had met several days earlier and decided to travel together. They were from two of the other provinces in our empire. They graciously extended an invitation for us to join them.

When we reached the Mediterranean Sea, it was obvious that the star was leading us south into Judaea. The star appeared to be getting brighter – and though I knew better, it appeared to be inviting us to follow it. As we discussed our course of action, we determined that we should travel to Jerusalem. We were told that King Herod was in residence in Jerusalem; therefore, we would stop there, pay homage to him, and inquire as to the birthplace of the King.

As we road into Jerusalem, our arrival created quite a stir. The Jews are a more austere people, whereas we Parthians tend to be somewhat flamboyant in our attire and demeanor. The size of our traveling party also drew attention. People apparently thought we were a royal delegation sent on official business to their king.

The people began to flock around us as we made our way closer to the palace. We encountered two priests who appeared to hold positions of authority. We asked them if they could direct us to where the King of the Jews had been born. They looked at us incredulously and told us we would need to speak to King Herod.

Our welcome at the palace wasn't much different from what we had received from the crowd. People seemed to be greatly disturbed by our presence. Several questioned our servants as to why we did not bring the gifts we were carrying into the palace. We were hurriedly brought before King Herod. I asked him, *"Where is He who has been born King of the Jews? For we saw His star when it rose and have come to worship Him."*[1] The king appeared to be troubled by my question, as if this was the first he had heard of it. He told us to remain where we were as he exited the room.

He was gone for quite a while, and we were left unattended. This was an unusual royal visit! Finally, when he returned, he asked us when the star had first appeared. We told him about a year ago. He told us that aligned with what he had seen – though I honestly doubted if he had even seen the star until we mentioned it to him.

He told us that the baby had been born in Bethlehem. That information aligned with what I had studied in the Hebrew writings. But then he said, *"Go and search diligently for the Child, and when you have found Him, bring me word, that I too may come and worship Him."*[2]

It seemed strange that he would wait for us to find the King and then return with a report. I couldn't help thinking that we Parthians appeared to be more interested in paying homage to their newborn King than the Jews themselves. As we left, we again saw the star rise, leading us to continue our journey.

.   .   .

When we arrived in Bethlehem, we knew better than to ask any of the townspeople where the baby was – especially after our reception in Jerusalem. So, we watched the star as it came to rest over a house built beside a hill. The master of the home greeted us when we knocked on the door. He told us his name was Achim. He looked astounded by our appearance.

"Greetings, strangers. What is your business here?" he asked.

I explained that we were seeking the newborn King of the Jews and that the star had led us to his home. A woman, who was apparently his wife, stepped out from behind him and told us to follow her. As we entered the courtyard of the home, the other people inside also seemed astonished by our presence. If there was truly a newborn King in this house, they were not expecting Him to have any visitors!

We followed the woman up to a small, plain room on the third floor. She remained outside the doorway but pointed for us to enter. Inside, we saw a baby who appeared to be about six weeks old, together with His young mother. The mother and child were dressed plainly, and the room was furnished very simply.

This was a surprising abode for One who is a King. But there was an atmosphere in the room that was undeniable. We immediately knew we were in the presence of royalty and that this was the child! The mother was the first person we had encountered in all of Judaea who was not surprised to see us. It was as if she were expecting us. She gave us a knowing look and nodded for us to enter. Immediately, we fell down and worshipped the baby.

After a time, we sent word to our servants to bring up the gifts we had brought. I presented the gift of frankincense. As we opened the boxes, their aromatic scent filled the room … the entire house … and the street below. Next, one of my companions presented his gift of gold – gold that was fit for a King. Finally, another companion presented the gift of myrrh. Myrrh was well-known for its medicinal qualities. The oil also emitted a fragrant scent that mixed well with frankincense.

There was a hushed reverence in the room and few words were spoken. We learned the young mother's husband was away on business in Jerusalem. She asked us how we had found the child. We explained about the star and told her how it had appeared and how we had been watching for a celestial sign. She listened intently to every word we spoke, but her only response was a gentle, understanding smile.

As we prepared to leave, the child's mother thanked us for coming and honoring her Son. She bid us God's blessing as we continued on our journey. Without any further ado, we departed.

We decided to camp in the hills outside Bethlehem for the night since it was late. We would return to Jerusalem the next day to bring our report back to King Herod. However, that night we all had the same dream – we were warned not to return to Herod. We were warned that he only sought to harm the child. So, in the morning, we decided to return to our provinces by a different route.

We feared for the baby and His parents if Herod found them. But something told us He never would. As we traveled, our hearts rejoiced because we knew we had seen the One whose coming had been foretold so long ago. No other King has ever been born under a star like this One. He will be a King like no other. He is truly the King of kings. And one day at His feet every knee will bow.

Little did I know how true that would be ...

〜

ELIEZER – THE SON

I am Achim and Miriam's youngest son, Eliezer. My parents named me after the prophet who boldly rebuked our ancestor King Jehoshaphat near the end of his life for aligning himself with King Ahaziah of Israel in disobedience to God. The prophet had bravely proclaimed truth even though it was unpopular, and my parents wanted me to be mindful to always do the same.

My wife Tamar, my infant son, Daniel, and I live here in the home of my parents. Both of my brothers and their families live here, too. After I became betrothed to Tamar, my father and I built a room on the second floor of our home so she and I would have a space of our own after we were married. I was proud to bring Tamar into our home after the wedding feast.

Daniel is now one year old. We're already talking about building another room for him and his future brothers. This home has grown a lot since my brothers and I were young boys sharing one room.

Like my father and my two older brothers, I am a carpenter. Currently all four of us are working for the temple priests in Jerusalem. We are adding rooms to their administrative quarters on the Royal Porch. Even though the reconstruction work of the temple under King Herod the Great was completed a few years ago, there are always additions and changes that the priests want made.

As long as the temple treasury is able to pay us, we are more than happy to oblige. I am grateful that we are able to leave for Jerusalem just before sunrise each day, get in a good day's work, and still be back home with our families in time for our evening meal. Occasionally we stay in Jerusalem overnight, but we try to avoid that as much as possible.

For weeks, my parents and the rest of us busily made preparations for the arrival of our extended family coming to town to register for the census. It was hard to believe that such a mundane thing as a government census could bring so much joy. And I would add that is the only joy that Roman rule has brought us!

My parents were particularly glad that my father's cousin Joseph would be with us. They spoke of it on several occasions. In preparation, we had built an additional room on the third floor of our home just for him. It would also be used by our expanding family in the days ahead – but Joseph would be the first guest to sleep in the room. I had met him when I was a young boy, and I had seen him last spring in Jerusalem for Passover. I was looking forward to getting to know him better.

That's why I was so surprised when one night my father told us that Joseph wouldn't be staying with us. One of our other guests mentioned that he had seen Joseph's brother Clopas. Clopas and his wife, Mary, were staying in the home of her sister – one of our other family members. My father didn't give any explanation for Joseph's absence. He and my mother glanced at each other, but nothing more was said.

That night as the rest of our guests arrived, my father insisted on stabling their animals. My brothers and I offered to help, but he would not hear of it. It seemed odd, but we knew that our father always had a reason for everything he did, so we said nothing more. We helped our guests get settled in their rooms. We had moved all of our children together so there was just enough room. We even had one room left over – the one that had been intended for Joseph.

The next day, I sensed tension between my parents. I decided it must be the stress of hosting so many people, even though that seemed out of character. We all made our way to our local synagogue to register for the census.

As I was leaving home, the shepherd's son Shimon stopped me and asked about the family who had been in our stable the night before. I told him I didn't know who he was talking about. There hadn't been anyone in our stable to the best of my knowledge. He was adamant and kept asking me their names and where they had gone. I told him I had no idea who he was talking about. Eventually, he left.

When I arrived at the synagogue, I noticed someone had written "Joseph, son of Jacob, from Nazareth" in the registry. By his name was written, "his wife Mary and newborn son, Jesus." I was certain that wasn't our cousin Joseph because he wasn't married yet – but I wondered who this could be.

I saw our cousin Clopas and went over to greet him. His young son James was with him. I asked about his brother Joseph, but Clopas explained he had unexpectedly been called away shortly after they arrived in town. So, I asked him to pass along my regards and that I regretted not being able to enjoy Joseph's company.

About a week later during dinner, Tamar mentioned to my mother that she thought she had heard a baby crying on the third floor. I immediately commented with a chuckle that I kept hearing cries coming from all over our home. Between our guests and their infants, as well as my brothers' families, there was no shortage of crying babies in our home these days.

· · ·

"It's difficult to tell from where all the cries are coming," my mother responded. "But each one is a delight." And then she changed the subject.

Another month passed. The census registration was completed. All of our guests had long since departed for home, and our lives had returned to normal. The temple priests kept adding to the work they wanted us to do on the administrative quarters. They demanded we have one of the rooms finished the next day. That meant one of us would need to stay in Jerusalem and work through the night. My father and brothers had already stayed, so I agreed it was my turn. I told them goodbye and continued with my work.

After several hours, I needed to get some fresh air. I walked through the Court of the Gentiles. Only a handful of people were walking around this time of night, but I came upon an older man who appeared to be praying. He looked familiar, and as I came closer I realized it was Joseph. He was praying earnestly and didn't notice me. As much as I wanted to speak with him and learn if everything was okay, I did not want to interrupt his prayer time.

I waited for a while, but he continued praying. I went back to work but regretted not being able to talk with him. I, like the rest of my family, was concerned for him. The next morning, I told my father and brothers about seeing Joseph. My father did not seem that interested, so the conversation went no further.

Normally, this would not have seemed odd except for what happened last evening. As usual, our household had retired early for the night. But I was restless and couldn't sleep. I heard a quiet knock at the entry to our home. I was preparing to answer it when I heard my father say, "Greetings, strangers. What is your business here?"

The response was somewhat muffled. I saw my mother step from behind my father and tell the visitors to follow her. What I saw next amazed me!

It was a regal processional dressed in colorful, royal attire. There were about a dozen men, plus servants. The servants did not enter at first but were later summoned to bring in three chests that appeared to be heavy. My mother quietly led the men up to the empty room on the third floor.

My father did not join them, but it was obvious he was curious why they had come. I was surprised that he allowed these men to enter our home and follow my mother. The two of them obviously knew something I did not. And I was going to remedy that. I decided to keep a watchful eye on them!

Only a few of the men could fit in the room at one time. As my mother opened the door, the light of a solitary lamp spilled out into the hallway. Initially, the first three men stood quietly with rapt attention focused on something – or someone – in the room. Within a matter of moments, these stately men fell to their knees and bowed their heads as if to worship. They remained kneeling for a while before they called for their servants to bring in the chests they had brought.

When the first chest was opened the sweet fragrance of frankincense began to waft out of the room. I had only smelled the fragrance once before. It was not common in our circles. But soon the soothing richness of its scent permeated our entire home. Next, they opened a chest that glistened in the lamp light. It was a chest filled with gold! They obviously were presenting these gifts to someone. But who was it? And why were they in our upper room?

They subsequently opened a chest with a third gift. It, too, emitted a fragrant scent. I had encountered this scent before. It was commonly used to prepare a body for the grave or for medicinal purposes. This chest was filled with myrrh. After the gifts were presented, the first three men stepped out of the room so the next three could enter. Each group lingered on their knees for a while before exiting, until finally all of the visitors had been in the room.

· · ·

The room was silent until I heard a woman's voice – a voice that was not familiar to me. She asked the men how they had found the child. So, there *was* a child in the room! Tamar *had* heard a baby crying! And these men had come to worship this baby! But, who was this child?

The visitors explained how they had followed a star. I had noticed a bright light in the sky, but I did not think it was unusual. But now these men were saying that the star led them to our home!

Eventually the men left, and my mother ushered them outside. The door to the upper room, however, remained open. I stepped out of my hiding place and walked to the open doorway. As I peered in, I saw a young woman holding a baby. The child was no older than six weeks. The mother looked up at me and, with a quiet nod, gave me permission to enter.

As I walked toward them, I immediately knew this was not just any child. I was immediately impressed that I needed to kneel. I didn't know who He was, but I knew He deserved my reverence.

Just then, I heard someone else enter the room. As I looked back, I saw it was my father. Slowly and reverently, he walked into the room. When he came closer, he also fell to his knees. And then he began to weep. Quietly at first, but then he began to cry uncontrollably.

"I am so sorry, Mary," he said between sobs. "I am so sorry I did not believe you and Joseph. I have thought and spoken evil of you, when all you two did was be faithful servants to our God. I refused you entry into my home! I refused entry to the child of the Living God! I turned my back on you – and Him! Mary, please forgive me!" Then he turned his gaze on the baby and said, "My God, please forgive me!"

My mother entered the room and quickly knelt beside my father, embracing him. Then we all bowed before the baby. I asked His name.

"Jesus," Mary replied. I immediately remembered the entry I had seen on the census registration.

By now, our entire household was awake. I looked around and saw Tamar, my brothers and their wives, as well as some of the older children. Tamar came and knelt beside me. We couldn't all fit in the room. Some of the family spilled out into the hallway, but we all gathered in worship.

Mary told us the story of how the angel Gabriel had come to her. She told us about the events that had led to today, including the visits from the shepherds and the magi. God had heralded the birth of His Son, right here in our midst – and we hadn't had eyes to see or hearts to receive – until now!

My mother embraced Mary, as did Tamar and my two sisters-in-law. Each one took turns holding the baby and gazed into His welcoming eyes. We all knew our lives would never be the same. It was a night that will forever be etched in our hearts.

Joseph arrived early the next morning. Mary's days of purification were now complete. It was time for them to go to the temple in Jerusalem and bring their offerings for purification and redemption. From there, they would return home.

Joseph and my father embraced as my father wept and spoke quietly in his ear. It would be several days before we all knew what had truly transpired. But whatever the misunderstandings were, it appeared that hearts had been mended. However, we regretted not having more time to spend with Mary and Jesus. We were all sad to see them leave.

Since my father, brothers, and I were also headed to Jerusalem, we traveled with Joseph and his family to the temple. My father gave Joseph one of our donkeys so they could transport the gifts from the magi. We embraced and then left them to continue to the temple. As we parted, we promised to see one another in the spring in Jerusalem for the Passover.

Little did I know that we would not see each other at the next Passover. God had a different journey planned for His Son ...

LEVI – THE RABBI

I am Levi, the chief rabbi in Bethlehem. Before you become too impressed with my position, remember that Bethlehem is ordinarily a small town – when the census is not taking place – and there are only three rabbis in our synagogue.

During my younger days, I was a student of Hillel the Elder in Jerusalem. Hillel is still recognized as the highest authority on all spiritual matters among the Pharisees. I remember fondly those days as his student. My friend Gamaliel and I would sit at the feet of our master for hours on end discussing – and at times debating – the finer points of our written Scripture and our oral traditions.

These are the guide for our daily lives as Jews. And my role as a rabbi is not only to teach those truths, but also to be a counselor, a role model, and a guide. I am grateful to Jehovah God for the opportunity to serve Him and guide the people of Bethlehem in following Him.

My personal passion is the study of the prophetic writings – particularly those that talk about the coming of the Messiah. It has been four hundred years since the last prophetic writing, the Book of Malachi, was written.

The prophet predicts the coming of a messenger who will clear the way for the Messiah. There was a time I thought that messenger might be Hillel because of his wisdom and understanding. But he himself acknowledged that he is not the one. We still await the messenger – who will soon be followed by the Messiah.

Even when the Book of Malachi was written, we were under the rule of conquerors. In that day, it was the Persians. Today, it is the Romans. So, we continue to hunger and hope for the arrival of our Messiah to deliver us from the bondage of pagan rule. I wake up each morning hoping it will be the day the Messiah comes.

And I am in the right place to watch for His arrival. The prophet Micah wrote, *"But you, O Bethlehem Ephrathah, are only a small village in Judah. Yet a ruler of Israel will come from you, One whose origins are from the distant past."*[1] The Messiah will come from Bethlehem! Could He already be here? Each day I wait and watch!

Today, I returned to Jerusalem for the celebration of Hillel's 107th birthday as I have done for the past eighteen years I have lived in Bethlehem. It is a rare privilege and blessing to honor this one whom God has seen fit to grant with such a long life. But today, there was something even more unique – and more important – about my time in Jerusalem. Before I tell you what happened, I must first recount some of the events of the past few weeks.

Six weeks ago, I was out unusually late. I rarely have trouble sleeping, but that night I was restless. I decided the best remedy was to go for a walk through town in the hopes it would tire me out. It was a cool, clear night. The stars were shining brightly so I could see clearly.

It was well after midnight when I saw a group of shepherds. They were leaving town and going back to their fields – but I could not help but see their jubilance. One of the shepherds named Moshe told me they had just come from visiting a baby. He told me the most amazing story about an angel who had come to him and the others earlier that night while they were watching over their flocks. The angel announced that the Messiah had been born that night in Bethlehem.

Moshe went on to explain that the angel had been joined by a large celestial host that had praised God in the announcement of the baby's birth. The shepherds decided to come to town to see the baby for themselves. They had worshipped the baby and now were returning to their fields.

I could not refute their enthusiasm. They truly believed what they were telling me. As they departed, they directed me to the stable where the baby had been born and told me to go see for myself. But as wonderful as their story sounded, I couldn't help but question some of the obvious problems with their account.

First, angels had not been seen for hundreds of years. It was hard to imagine that God was sending angels to earth.

Second, if these really were angels, why would they choose to announce the birth of the Messiah to shepherds on a hill? I had spent most of my life studying the prophecies and I had been watching every day. Honestly, if anyone was going to see the arrival of the Messiah it was me. I knew exactly what to look for! Surely, Jehovah God would not entrust such an announcement to a group of uneducated shepherds! He would give that news to men who had been educated in His Scriptures.

Third, the Messiah would not be ushered into the world in an animal's stable! We were talking about the King of kings! Such an idea was preposterous. I wondered if maybe the shepherds had consumed too much wine that evening. If a baby had been born that night, of course it was cause for celebration – but saying that the baby was the Messiah was just too hard to believe.

. . .

I wrote off their announcements to the ramblings of well-meaning men with very active imaginations and continued with my walk through town. There was no need to seek out a stable! I decided to put their ramblings out of my mind.

Over the next few days, I did not hear anyone else in town talking about a baby in a stable. No one else had experienced angelic visitations. No one was announcing the birth of the Son of God. As a matter of fact, no one had announced the birth of any son since the birth of Moshe's newborn son, Eliezer. As the chief rabbi, I was always alerted about the birth of any baby in town – for the purpose of spiritual blessing, if nothing else. But no announcement came. No baby had been born. Perhaps the Messiah will come tomorrow, I thought. I would continue to wait!

I thought nothing more about it until one week later. A stranger came into the synagogue. He told me his name was Joseph and he was from Nazareth. He had come to Bethlehem with his young wife and she had given birth to a son eight days ago. He went on to explain that he was working in Jerusalem while his wife was recovering in Bethlehem.

"The baby is eight days old today," the man said. "We have no place to circumcise the child. Would you circumcise Him here in the synagogue?" He was carrying the baby in his arms swaddled in cloth.

I told him I would be honored to do so. I asked the child's name, and he proudly declared, "His name is Jesus!" Since a rabbi is not only a spiritual leader, but also is often called upon to assist with medical needs, I have often been asked to circumcise baby boys. So, there was nothing unusual about this request. I recounted the covenant that God had made with Abraham and that through circumcision, this child was entering into that covenant.

After Joseph left with the child, I thought of the shepherds. Was this the baby they had seen in the stable? This family obviously did not live here. Perhaps they had nowhere to stay that night. And there would have been no reason for anyone to tell me about His birth at the time. But now that I'd seen the baby, I didn't detect anything special about Him. If He was the Messiah, the father had made no such pronouncement. Again, I dismissed the thought.

That was five weeks ago. But last night something unusual happened. I was having trouble sleeping again so I went walking through town. To my amazement I came upon a royal processional! I could tell from their attire and bearing that they were from the east. "These men must be lost," I thought. "Surely, they are traveling to Jerusalem to see the King. No such group of men has good reason to be in Bethlehem." But they appeared to know exactly where they were going.

Curiosity got the best of me so I followed them. They stopped at the home of Achim the carpenter. After exchanging a few words, I saw Achim's wife usher the entire party inside. The visitors' servants removed chests from their pack animals and brought them into the home. It appeared the men were coming for an audience with someone … in Bethlehem … in a carpenter's home.

I decided to wait in the shadows and keep watch on what they did. They remained in the house for quite some time. When they finally exited, I noticed the servants were no longer carrying the chests. I could faintly hear some of what they were saying. But one thing I heard clearly as they passed me on their camels – "Truly, He is the King of kings." I kept thinking about that statement as I made my way home.

That brings me to today. I left Bethlehem early this morning to make my way here to Jerusalem. As I arrived at the temple, I saw Achim and his sons. They were with Joseph and a young woman who must be the baby's mother. Among their animals was a donkey bearing the chests I had seen the servants carry into Achim's home.

At that moment, it all began to make sense. The shepherds. The announcement they had heard from an angel. Royalty from the east who acknowledged a King of kings. The prophecy from Micah. And then my own words came back to me, "If anyone was going to see the arrival of the Messiah it would be me. I would know exactly what to look for!" Perhaps I didn't know what to look for – but God had caused me to be restless two times in order to see those who had known what to look for!

And God, by His grace, had permitted me to circumcise the child! But He didn't need to be circumcised to enter into the covenant – He is the fulfillment of the covenant! God had permitted me to see the One for whom I had waited and watched.

As the parents and child entered the temple to bring their offerings of purification and redemption, I realized that this first-born Son does not need to be redeemed – He has come to redeem us! I wanted to shout the words throughout the temple, but God quickened my spirit that it was not my news to tell. He would reveal His Son in His way and in His time. As I stood there watching, I praised God and worshipped Him and His Son.

When I arrived at Hillel's birthday celebration, I thought about sharing this good news with him and with Gamaliel – but again I sensed God telling me not to do so. As Hillel made reference to the coming Messiah, it was all I could do not to tell them of His arrival. But that still small voice inside of me said, "His time has not yet come. I will reveal it in the proper time."

Little did I know what that would mean …

~

ANNAS – THE SCRIBE

$\mathcal{M}$y name is Annas and I am a young scribe serving in the court of King Herod the Great. I already have the ear of the king though I'm only nineteen years old. However, I am not content with my current position – my aspirations are much greater. I fully intend to be High Priest one day soon. But I have gotten ahead of myself. Let me start from the beginning.

My father, whose name was Seth, recently died. I am grateful to him for the life of privilege and political connection in which I was raised. With the advent of Roman administration over our land, the Sanhedrin was re-established. The Sanhedrin are our rabbinical courts, which have been established in every city of our land.

Since everything we do as Jews is guided by our religious laws and teachings, the courts are tasked with resolving any disputes or ruling on affairs that are in violation of our teachings. Our Roman rulers are concerned only with matters related to suspected rebellion or capital punishment. Therefore, the Sanhedrin is granted wide latitude in its decision-making process.

. . .

The Sanhedrin is divided into the Great Sanhedrin and the Lesser Sanhedrin. The Lesser Sanhedrin is made up of individual courts in each of our cities. The Great Sanhedrin serves as the supreme court of the land, taking appeals from cases decided by the lesser courts. My father was a member of the Great Sanhedrin. As such, he garnered significant influence and power.

I was an excellent student – not only under the teachings of my rabbis – but also the life teachings of my father. As I watched him and listened to him, I learned not only what to do, but also what not to do. My father became an ally of King Herod when he first rose to power under the Roman-given title of "King of the Jews." That alliance continued to strengthen over the years as Herod's grip of power over our land did the same.

Prior to the advent of Roman rule, two political influences dominated our land. One is the Pharisees, known for their doctrinal tenacity; the other is the Sadducees, known for their political savviness. Both groups are considered religious bodies, dividing most pointedly over their respective beliefs regarding the resurrection of the dead. There have always been good debates between the two bodies over that singular issue – and I venture those debates will always continue.

Sometimes I wonder if the debate is really over the issue of doctrine or the love of debate. My father was a Sadducee, as am I. Sadducees, because of our political alliance with the Herodian rulers, tend to carry the decision-making weight within the Sanhedrin.

Being a Sadducee fits me well. I am more politically and socially motivated than spiritually. My tendency is to use spiritual beliefs for political advantage. The current High Priest is a friend of my father by the name of Eleazar ben Boethus. He, too, is a Sadducee. Through his relationship with my father, and through my own cunning, I achieved the role of a scribe to the Great Sanhedrin.

. . .

Though my role is to give counsel to the members and not be a decision-maker myself, it has placed me in a position of influence over those who are making decisions – and the decisions they make. I am the youngest person to have ever held this position.

In recent years, King Herod has undertaken extensive building projects throughout our land. One of them was the reconstruction of our temple here in Jerusalem, which was completed just a few years ago. The other was the construction and establishment of a new port city along the Mediterranean Sea that he deftly named Caesarea Maritima. He established his palace and the seat of his governance in that showcase city. Caesarea has become our political capital, while Jerusalem remains the religious and accepted capital of our land.

I was honored when Eleazar ben Boethus gave me the choice of serving as a scribe in Herod's court in Caesarea or here in Jerusalem with the Sanhedrin. Despite any rulers' attempts to the contrary, I knew the center of power in our land would always be in Jerusalem. So, I determined to remain here.

But Herod also knows that the center of power is here, so periodically he comes here to stay at his palace in Jerusalem. I told Eleazar that I would be available to give counsel to the king as a scribe in his court whenever he was here. That way, I could maintain visibility in both centers of power.

Such was the case a week ago. Herod was staying in his palace here in Jerusalem, and I was attending him in his court. That afternoon, news reached the palace that a royal entourage from the east was making its way through the city in the direction of the palace. The king had not received any message that an envoy was coming. So, the surprise visit created quite an uproar in his court. Who had the audacity to show up at the king's door without royal permission or invitation? What matters could be so important that protocol would be so disregarded?

· · ·

The king decided to refuse them an audience, even before hearing their purpose. Even the Romans extended that courtesy to him! He had been told that this was a Parthian delegation. And he would not condescend to their breach in protocol.

I knew, however, how important our trade relations are with the Parthian empire. Also, they are our gateway to the Han Dynasty of China. We could ill-afford offending this strategic trade partner. Fortunately, over recent months, I had begun to develop a trusted relationship with Herod's son, Antipas. More than likely, he would one day become a ruler of our land when Herod died. So, our developing relationship would be invaluable in the days ahead – but it also was beneficial now.

I sought out Antipas, explained my assessment of the situation, and recommended that he counsel his father to accept the visitors. His powers of persuasion prevailed, and Herod agreed to grant an audience to the Parthian delegation. The king invited Antipas and me to join him in receiving them.

As the delegation entered the king's throne room, I was taken aback by one detail. I had been told they were bearing gifts befitting a king. And yet the servants reported to me that the gifts remained on their pack animals. The gifts obviously were not intended for this king!

The group was quite ostentatious – as Parthians tend to be. After they had dispensed with the prerequisite pleasantries, the magus by the name of Balthazar asked, *"Where is He who has been born King of the Jews? For we saw His star when it rose and have come to worship Him."*[1]

We were all taken off guard by their question. But to his credit, King Herod maintained his composure and instructed the delegation to remain in his throne room while he momentarily excused himself to go get the information they wanted. His composure quickly faded once the three of us were standing in the privacy of his personal chambers.

. . .

"The King of the Jews!" he ranted. "I am the King of the Jews! How dare they suggest that anyone apart from me has been born into those ranks! Antipas, my son, you are one of my heirs. Has news of your birth taken seventeen years to make its way to Babylon? How dare these people suggest that one has been born who will displace me and my seed!"

I realized that calmer heads needed to prevail, so I said, "Your majesty, though you were not born a Jew yourself, you are well-versed in our Scriptures and our prophecies. You know that the prophets foretell of One who will come – the Messiah – who will lead our people to rebel against foreign authority and return our nation to its position of glory.

"Our people have prayed for His arrival for hundreds of years. Perhaps these magi have read those writings and seek that One. If truly that prophecy has come to pass, your Majesty will want to know – so that you are able to preserve your own position of authority within the kingdom.

"As I recall, the prophets foretold that such a One will arise out of the town of Bethlehem. Would the King not be prudent to advise the Parthians to seek the Christ there? And if by chance they find such a One, they could return to tell you of their finding. Then you could determine what further action, if any, you need to undertake. That is, if it pleases your Majesty."

The king's rage began to subside as he warmed to my suggestion. Antipas added his endorsement to the plan. I arranged to have one of the priests brought to the king's throne room to read the ancient prophecy to our guests as they stood before our king.

We returned to the throne room, where the priest repeated the prophecy at the king's request:

"The Christ will be born *in Bethlehem of Judea, for so it is written by the prophet: 'And you, O Bethlehem, in the land of Judah, are by no means least among the rulers of Judah; for from you shall come a ruler who will shepherd My people Israel.'"*[2]

King Herod then turned to the magi and told them, *"Go and search diligently for the child, and when you have found him, bring me word, that I too may come and worship him."*[3] That last statement seemed to ingratiate the king with the magi.

After the men departed, Herod was quite pleased with himself. If these Parthian magi did in fact find that such a child had been born, they would tell him about it – and he would do what needed to be done. And if, more likely, they did not find a child, then Herod would be seen as magnanimous in his response and the Parthians foolish in their expedition. It truly was a "win-win" situation for King Herod. He was very pleased that he had come up with the plan. And I was pleased that he thought it was his plan!

For the next several days, Herod walked around the palace quite delighted with himself. On several occasions, he asked if there had been any word from the Parthian magi. The longer they delayed in their return, the more certain he was that their expedition had been fruitless. Obviously, they didn't want to admit their error – or so he thought.

After several more days passed, I decided to send out spies to find out what the magi were doing and why they had not returned. The spies returned the next day and gave me their report.

I sought out Antipas and together we requested an audience with the king. "The Parthians did in fact make their way to Bethlehem as the king directed, your Majesty," I said. "Several people witnessed their arrival. But no one could tell our spies if they visited anyone or saw a child while they were there. They apparently camped for the night on one of the hills overlooking the town. The next morning they departed. But instead of returning by way of Jerusalem to bring you a report, your Majesty, they traveled due east through the Arabian desert in order to avoid you. They obviously will not be returning to bring you any report."

"I knew it!" King Herod responded. "Those Parthians, who thought they knew something we did not, discovered their error and were too embarrassed to return to me to admit it. I will use their disrespect to my advantage in the days ahead!"

"You see Annas, there was no cause for concern," the king continued. "Our plan was successful, and we will reap the benefits in the days to come."

"But your Majesty," I replied, "there is one other matter. Apparently, the gifts the magi brought with them to give the newborn King remained in Bethlehem! Our spies learned that when the magi departed the next morning, their pack animals were not carrying any of the chests. The men must have given them to their intended recipient – but our spies were not able to learn who that recipient is!"

King Herod once again flew into a rage!

Little did I know that one day – many years later – I would come face-to-face with the One who had been the recipient of those gifts …

∾

SIMEON – THE ANCIENT

*M*y name is Simeon and I have lived a long and full life. On my last birthday, I turned one hundred thirteen years old. I know that you're going to tell me that I don't look a day over one hundred – so I will tell you my secret to looking so youthful. It's figs! Most every day of my life I have eaten a fig. I recommend them highly!

But, in all seriousness, I will tell you the real secret to my longevity. When I was young, the Spirit of God gave me a promise. He told me I would not see death before I had seen the promised Messiah. Each day since I have lived expectantly – awaiting the fulfillment of God's promise to me – knowing that He does not lie. That which God has promised will come to pass!

I have also lived assuredly, knowing that I was immortal until the day of the blessed event. Today is that very day! But before I tell you about the events of this day, allow me to go back to the day that God gave me His promise.

When I was a lad, the emperor of Rome did not rule over us. About fifty years before I was born, a priest by the name of Judas Maccabeus led our people in a revolt against the Syrian ruler, Antiochus, who had attempted to eradicate our religious practices and destroy our faith in Jehovah God.

Though our people had endured foreign pagan rule for over five hundred years leading up to that moment, the desecrations committed by Antiochus catalyzed our people in a revolt that led to independence. The temple here in Jerusalem was recovered from the control of our enemies and was reconsecrated for its one true purpose.

A new altar was built to replace the one that had been desecrated, and new holy vessels were made. The fire on the altar was rekindled and the lamps of the candlesticks were lit. However, unadulterated, undefiled, pure olive oil with the seal of the high priest was needed for the lampstand, and it was required to burn throughout the night every night. But they could only locate one flask of oil, which would be sufficient for only one day.

It took eight days to prepare a fresh supply of pure oil for the lampstand. And, yet, that one day's supply of oil kept the lampstand burning for eight days until the new oil was ready. As the lampstand continued to burn, the dedication of the altar was celebrated for eight days with sacrifices and song.

Every year since, we remember those eight days of reconsecration of the temple and the miracle of the oil through an eight-day Festival of Lights, often called Hanukkah.

In the years that followed, our people struggled to maintain independence under the rule of our two leadership bodies – the Sadducees and the Pharisees. Attempts were made to enter into a peaceful alliance with the Roman Republic in an effort to discourage other potential oppressors seeking to lay siege.

. . .

Ultimately though, when I was about fifty years old, we became a protectorate of Rome under the administration of a client government. King Herod the Tetrarch was installed as the "King of the Jews" by the Roman senate about forty years ago. He replaced the last king of the Hasmonean dynasty that had ruled throughout the years of our fragile independence. Herod may now be our "king," but Rome has the last word over our lives.

I was born during that brief period of independence. Our home was in Jerusalem, and I have lived in this city my entire life. I have always worshipped here in the temple. I have participated in every one of our feasts and festivals since I was old enough to do so. I always seek to honor God in everything I do.

My father was a Pharisee. He was considered by most to be a righteous man. Many also considered him to be a patriot. I knew him as a man of deep conviction who sought after God with all of his heart. He knew that we were God's chosen people – set apart for His divine purpose.

My father always gave praise to God for our freedom from Syrian rule, but he knew our freedom was precarious. He often told me, "Simeon, we will not have lasting peace until the day the Messiah comes to rule over us. On that day the enemies of God will be defeated forever, and we will have peace for all eternity!"

My father would often recite the promise of the coming Messiah as foretold by the prophet Isaiah:

For to us a Child is born, to us a Son is given; and the government shall be upon His shoulder, and His name shall be called Wonderful Counselor, Mighty God, Everlasting Father, Prince of Peace. Of the increase of His government and of peace there will be no end, on the throne of David and over His kingdom, to establish it and to uphold it with justice and with righteousness from this time forth and forevermore. [1]

My father longed for that day and he placed within me a burning passion for that day, as well. Then one day, God gave me a promise. It was the year of my sixteenth birthday. I was in the temple praying during the Festival of Lights. I was praising God for His goodness and His mercy and thanking Him for His grace. I was praying that God would send His Promised One so our people would remain free.

In celebration of the festival, light was shining throughout the temple. As I prayed, I heard an audible voice call out to me saying, "Simeon, you will not depart from this world until you have witnessed My promise fulfilled. You will see the child of whom Isaiah wrote. You will see the Son whom I will send. You will see the Light that will never grow dark – not just for eight days, but for all of eternity! Watch for Him and wait for Him!"

I'll never forget the look on my father's face when I told him what I had heard. "Simeon," he said, "God has answered my prayer! He has said that though I may not see the Messiah in my lifetime, you will! The Spirit of God has spoken to you. Remember His promise. No matter what happens in the days ahead, watch for the child. He will come!"

Much has happened since that day. My father passed away long ago. The Romans came to rule our land. The temple was rebuilt by Herod to rival the majesty of Solomon's Temple – and is now much grander than what it was when I was a boy. God has blessed me with many sons, grandsons, and great-grandsons – all of whom have hearts that seek to honor Him. But as the years passed, even my family questioned if God would fulfill His promise to me – or if I merely dreamed it.

I have come to the temple every day looking for the child. Recently, my great-grandson, Ashriel, has accompanied me since I am unsteady on my feet. He leads me to a seat in the outer court so I can see everyone as they enter or leave the temple.

That brings me to today! This morning, soon after I was settled in my seat, I saw a young woman carrying an infant. I could tell the man with her was obviously her husband. He was attentive to every need of the young mother and the baby in her arms. I saw the man as he approached one of the temple merchants in the outer court to purchase a pair of turtledoves. He then presented the turtledoves and five shekels to the priest as an offering.

I knew that in accordance with our law the baby must be a boy. I also knew that He was forty days old. Our law requires that a woman bring a sin offering to the temple for purification[2] when her child is forty days old – thus the two turtledoves. But our law also requires that the first-born son be redeemed with an offering – thus the five shekels.[3]

As I watched the family, I began to wonder whether this child was the One. For the first time in almost one hundred years, my heart began to pound. I knew in my spirit that this was the child! I told Ashriel to help me walk quickly over to the family.

My actions must have seemed curious to them, but they graciously turned their young Son so I could look into His eyes. I immediately knew this was the child! This was the One whose coming had been promised. Tears of joy streamed down my cheeks! With my eyes opened wide, I turned to the baby's mother and said:

"Behold, this Child is appointed for the fall and rising of many in Israel, and for a sign that is opposed and for a sword that will pierce through your own soul also, so that thoughts from many hearts may be revealed."[4]

She didn't utter a word but simply thought about what I said and nodded. I was struck by her tenderness. I could see why Jehovah God chose her to be the mother of His Son. When I reached to pick up the baby, she willingly handed Him to me.

As I held Him, I looked heavenward and said, *"Lord, now You are letting Your servant depart in peace, according to Your word; for my eyes have seen*

Your salvation that You have prepared in the presence of all peoples, a light for revelation to the Gentiles, and for glory to Your people Israel."[5]

I returned the child to His mother's arms and blessed her and the father. An event I had waited for most of my life had only lasted a few moments, but the fulfillment of God's promise would last for eternity. As the rest of the people in the temple went about their business, they were oblivious to Who was in their presence or the significance of what had just occurred.

Sadly, this probably wouldn't be the last time – even in this very place. But their unawareness doesn't change the promise, and it doesn't make its fulfillment any less. The sacrifice being offered up today wasn't so much the two turtledoves presented by the child's earthly parents, the true sacrifice was the child being given by His Heavenly Father.

Little did I know how great that sacrifice would be …

~

ANNA – THE PROPHETESS

$\mathcal{I}$ am Anna, considered by some to be a prophetess – which means God has granted me the gift of hearing His voice and speaking His Word. In many respects, it is more of a responsibility than a gift. Long ago, God showed me I was to speak the message He gave me to the person He wanted to receive it – regardless of how that person reacted.

I grew up in the city of Hebron. While I was still very young, my father, Phanuel the Asherite, entered into an agreement with Abdiel the Levite for me to marry his son Menachem. My parents were already old when my mother gave birth to me, so they wanted to be certain that my future was secure.

Menachem was several years older than I was and already a priest of the division of Abijah, just like his father. We married when I was fourteen years old. And from that first day, there was never any doubt that Menachem loved me. But he also showed me that he loved God with all of his heart. And he taught me how to love God with all of my heart, soul, and mind. Those were not just words to him – he lived them out!

. . .

My mother gave me a white tunic she had woven in one piece without any seams for a wedding present. It was the most beautiful garment I had ever seen. "Anna," my mother said, "this robe is for your firstborn son. Wrap him in it as a child, then preserve it and give it to him when he becomes a man." That precious gift became my most prized possession, and I looked forward to the day I would wrap my son in it.

But in the sovereignty of God, I never bore a child. My only regret in my marriage to Menachem was that I never gave him a son to carry on his name. But Menachem was always gracious. He often reminded me that we would trust God and rest in the peace of His plan for our lives. Our love for Him and for one another filled our hearts and kept them from aching for the child we would never have.

We journeyed to Jerusalem multiple times each year for Menachem to serve in the temple. Each division of priests served in the temple for two one-week periods every year, as well as during our three major annual feasts of Passover, Pentecost, and Tabernacles. The priests were to offer daily sacrifices and to convey priestly blessings.

Menachem counted it an honor and a privilege to stand before God on behalf of the people. He loved his Lord. He loved his wife. And he loved his work. He was greatly encouraged when his brother Zechariah began to sense God's calling to also serve as a priest. Though Zechariah was fifteen years younger than Menachem, my husband looked forward to mentoring and training his brother. Our life was filled with joy and purpose. I could not imagine anything better.

Menachem lived each day believing it might be the day of the Messiah's coming. He not only knew and believed the prophecies, he looked forward to them through eyes of faith. And he taught me to do the same. I came to believe that God would grant me the opportunity to see the arrival of His Son with my own eyes. We didn't know how or when, but we believed the time was drawing near.

· · ·

When we had been married about seven years, we went to Jerusalem again for a time of service. This occasion was particularly significant to Menachem. He had been selected to present the offering of incense on the altar in the sanctuary. It was a rare privilege and one he was looking forward to later in the week.

We were staying in one of the small chamber apartments reserved for priests in the outer courts. Menachem usually woke up before I did, so I was surprised to see he was still fast asleep that morning. He did not even stir once I began moving about our small room. When I went over to wake him, he was cold to my touch. I quickly realized he was not breathing.

My husband had peacefully died in his sleep. I called out to the other priests and their wives in the adjoining apartments. They quickly came to comfort me and attend to Menachem's body. I was so grateful for their care and compassion; they even took care of all of the arrangements.

My husband had not been ill. We had been planning for a day of ministry at the temple. Little had I known when I lay down to sleep the night before that I would bury my husband the next day. Though we had been scheduled to only use the apartment until the end of the week, the High Priest Aristobulus II told me I could stay as long as I needed.

I was a twenty-one-year-old widow, not much more than a child myself. My parents had died soon after Menachem and I were married, so returning to their home was not an option. However, I was blessed by the way so many ministered to me and attended to my needs.

Seven days following my husband's death, I sensed the angel of the Lord speaking to me in a dream that night. "Anna, thus saith the Lord, 'I am the God of your fathers and I am your God. *I know the plans I have for you; plans to prosper you and not to harm you, plans to give you hope and a future.*[1] I have known you since long before your mother gave birth to you. I gave you to your husband, and him to you, that you may know and experience the fullness of My love for you.

'I have placed within your heart an earnest expectancy for the coming of My Son. You will be a part of His story when He comes, and I will be with you all along the way. I will never leave you nor forsake you. You are not to remarry. Rather, draw close to Me and look to Me. I will be your comfort, your strength, your provision, and your peace. Serve Me here in My temple, ministering to those I bring to you. Worship Me with prayer and fasting. Listen to My voice and speak My words. Admonish each one I bring you to look forward to the day of the arrival of My Son. One day you will see Him. In the meantime, minister to each one I bring to you as if they were My Son.'"

I awoke the next morning with confidence. Mine was not to be a life of sorrow or regret but rather a life of devotion and unshakeable hope! I sought out the High Priest and told him what the angel of the Lord had told me. The High Priest said I could remain as a caretaker in the temple as the Lord had instructed me. In the six decades since, eight high priests have followed, and by the grace of God, each one has affirmed his support and my calling from the Lord.

In the years that followed, the temple was reconstructed and restored. The city of Jerusalem was conquered by the Romans and placed under their control. The city grew in size and splendor, and the number of people coming to the temple increased every year.

When some hear my story, they ask me why I did not remarry. I tell them because God told me not to. But I also share what else He told me – including to expect the arrival of the Messiah. I encourage them to watch faithfully and hopefully!

I have seen many widows neglected and exploited. Most, particularly those without children, have lived a life of poverty. But God kept His promise. He provided for me and cared for me – and has given me an unending joy. I still miss Menachem, but my Lord has been my close companion.

Menachem's brother Zechariah did become a priest. He later married a young woman by the name of Elizabeth who, as it turns out, was born on the very day my husband died. Over the years, I have watched God's faithfulness to them. And then, just a little over seven months ago – despite their advanced age – God blessed Elizabeth's barren womb by giving them a son.

Elizabeth confided to me that their son John is the one God has chosen to prepare the way for the coming Messiah. I saw them and their newborn son when they came to the temple to present their offering of redemption. My heart leapt, knowing that I will soon see the Son of God!

A friend of mine by the name of Simeon comes to the temple every day to wait expectantly for the Messiah. He watches every male child who is presented. He is now one hundred thirteen years old and has been waiting and watching for most of his life. I am eighty-four years old – but compared to him I am a youngster!

Then, this morning it happened! As I was walking through the temple, I noticed a young couple enter with their boy child. For some reason, my eye was drawn to them. The young woman, not much more than a child herself, was beautiful. Her husband walked beside her, paying close attention to her and their son. I was struck by his tenderness and humility. He reminded me of Menachem. I had seen many such tender arrivals at the temple over the years – but this one stood out.

I watched from a distance as they presented their offering to the priest. Then I heard the priest speak his words of blessing over the child. I continued watching as the man and woman lingered in the temple before turning to exit. Just then I saw Simeon approach them.

· · ·

But today, he didn't just look at the child and walk away. Tears were streaming down his face as he spoke with the man and the young mother. Then he placed his hand on the baby's head and spoke a blessing over Him. The mother and father watched and listened intently. As I looked at Simeon – and then at the child – I knew the Messiah had come!

God's timing is perfect! He had ordered my every step throughout my lifetime. He had allowed me to watch as He ordered the steps of those around me. Even the way He had ordered Menachem's steps – and his days. Now, He had ordered my steps this very day to witness the arrival of this family. I walked over and joined them in worship and praise of the one true God – the One who had ordered all of our steps from before the beginning of time.

The young mother graciously permitted me to hold the child. I spoke words of praise and blessing over Him. In my heart, I was that twenty-one-year-old, single woman who had been excitedly awaiting the arrival of the Messiah. And now, I was holding Him in my arms.

The young mother told me her story about the angel and what he had said. She told me about the shepherds and the magi. Her husband told me about the vision he had received in a dream that this child was the Son of God. But he also told me of a dream he had just the night before.

An angel of the Lord had appeared to him in that dream and said, *"Rise, take the Child and His mother and flee to Egypt, and remain there until I tell you, for Herod is about to search for the Child to destroy Him."*[2]

The child's father told me they were departing that very hour as God had instructed. He did not know where they would go in Egypt, but they would walk by faith. Jehovah God had ordered their every step in the advent of His Son – and He would continue to do so.

. . .

As I stood there with the child and His parents, I realized there was something I needed to do. I asked them to wait while I returned to my chamber and retrieved my most prized possession. As I handed the gift to the young mother, I said, "Wrap Him in this tunic and use it to keep Him warm. Then one day when He becomes a Man, give it to Him and tell Him about this day." His mother smiled at me sweetly and promised that she would.

I watched them leave the temple, and I knew I would never see them again – at least not in this life. But I looked to heaven and thanked God for His faithfulness and for this precious little One – the One who would save His people.

Little did I know how that salvation would come about, or how that seamless tunic would even be a part of that day ...

∽

ANTIPAS – THE PRINCE

J, Antipas, am a favored son of King Herod the Great. I grew up as a prince of the Herodian kingdom in the line of succession. The fact that I am a favored son is an important distinction. I was sixth in line for my father's throne. I am the second son of my father by his fourth wife, Malthace. I had one older brother, and four older half brothers by my father's three previous wives, and one younger half brother by his fifth wife.

No matter how complex your family relationships happen to be, trust me – mine are more complicated! As a matter of fact, my father had three of my older half brothers executed for what he called insurrection – all within four years of the events described below. Since my father had chosen to follow Jewish law and its dietary restrictions, the emperor of Rome, Caesar Augustus, was once heard to remark, "It is better to be Herod's pig than his son!" (A pig would never die at my father's hand.) So, we all knew to watch our father carefully!

My remaining older half brother, Herod II, and his beguiling wife, Herodias, were the apparent heirs to my father's throne. But my older brother Archelaus and I were working on a plan. We were going to convince our father to change his will so each of us would reign over portions of the kingdom following his death instead of Herod II.

I was seventeen at the time and had recently married my lovely wife, Phasaelis, a princess of Nabataea. The Nabataeans are a tribal kingdom situated to our east, centered around the city of Petra, south of the Parthian empire. It was a marriage of political convenience arranged by my father to solidify a treaty between our lands.

Regrettably, she and I never cared much for one another – particularly because I had my eye on my sister-in-law, Herodias. I could go into greater detail about our complex relationships, but I do not want to detract from this story.

Though my father had many faults, I always had great respect for him as a ruler. He was able to masterfully navigate through the political upheaval caused by a change in emperors and was able to assume his position with the strong backing of Rome. The Romans conquered our land twenty-seven years before my father was named the client-king of Rome.

Their rule was chaotic during those years, and our lands were languishing while the regions around us prospered. In the years following, though, my father led us in a time of aggressive rebuilding and prosperity. He developed strong alliances with the religious leadership, providing them with greater autonomy in their religious affairs and practices.

My plan was to build on what my father began. In fact, I worked at developing my own alliances with some of the rising Jewish leaders. One of those alliances was with a scribe named Annas in my father's court in Jerusalem. We are about the same age and we shared similar ambitions for the future. He had his eye on becoming the High Priest – and I intended to use my influence in the days ahead to help him achieve that goal.

. . .

He and I collaborated regarding a Parthian entourage of magi who had come to Jerusalem seeking a baby they believed was the One whose coming is foretold in the Jewish Scriptures. We encouraged my father to point the magi toward Bethlehem, with the understanding they would return to him and report what they discovered. If there truly was One born who people thought was their Messiah, He would threaten all of our plans.

My father was an old man – but I was not. And I did not intend to relinquish my throne to anyone. Allowing the Parthians to investigate and report back would give us the information necessary for us to act. If the rumor were false, we could publicly debunk it. If there was any truth to the rumor, we could take appropriate action while the child was still young. To again use the quote of Caesar Augustus, it may have been safer for the child if He was a pig!

The only flaw in our plan was that the Parthians did not return to give us a report. Annas sent out spies who reported that the magi had departed Bethlehem by way of the Arabian desert through the Nabataean kingdom in order to avoid returning through Jerusalem. They had intentionally chosen to avoid the king. That meant one of two things – either they did not find the child and did not want to admit it – or they found the child and decided against informing the king.

We thought it was the former reason until the spies reported the gifts the magi brought for the child had been left in Bethlehem. Now we believed the latter reason was true, but we were no closer to knowing who the child was or where He lived. I considered getting a message to the Nabataeans to ascertain what the magi had discovered, but by the time we learned of their deception, they had already passed through Nabataea.

My father's rage only increased as the months passed. I was convinced that if I could find a way to put an end to this supposed Messiah, I would solidify my position with my father – and he would not give the throne to my half brother. I would assure my position upon his death.

.   .   .

It was Annas who ultimately suggested we have all of the baby boys born in and around Bethlehem killed. Since the magi said they first saw a sign in the heavens about one year earlier, it made sense to execute those who were under two years of age. As much as I wanted to remove any potential threat to my future reign, the idea of killing innocent children made me somewhat ill. So, it took me a while to accept the plan. I knew my father would have no problem with the idea. After all, he had killed his own sons without giving it another thought.

Annas and I brought the recommendation before my father. As I suspected, he immediately embraced the idea. He called the centurion of his personal guard and told him a threat had been made against the throne. We would retaliate by executing all of the male children under two years old living in and immediately around Bethlehem.

The king instructed the centurion to lead a cadre of trusted cavalry guards to swiftly execute his orders. But, the soldiers were not to be told why they were executing the children.

That afternoon, the soldiers departed, riding majestically and bearing the colors of the Herodian guard. No one besides my father, Annas, and me knew the real reason for their mission – and no one else ever would!

The soldiers returned later that evening. The centurion reported that twenty boys had been executed. The father of one of the boys had also been killed when he attempted to fight. And since the soldiers arrived unexpectedly, half the children had already been murdered before the town realized what was taking place.

The wailing was deafening as the soldiers rode out of town. The centurion admitted that even though his soldiers were hardhearted men, this task had taken a toll on them. The king graciously agreed that the soldiers should be rewarded that night with an added portion of food and drink. Such was the price for twenty-one dead souls. Even I couldn't help but think to myself, "What have we become?"

. . .

Annas asked the centurion if there had been anything unusual at any of
the homes. Any extraordinary gatherings? Any uncommon gifts such as
gold or frankincense or myrrh? Were any of the children dressed in an
unusual way? Was anything out of place in the sleepy little town of Bethlehem? The centurion replied no to each question.

After my father dismissed the centurion, he announced, "Our plan was
successful! Our men caught the townspeople by surprise. The deed has
been done. The threat is averted. And none will be the wiser. The soldiers
acted under my authority and no one will dare to question the king."

"What about the Romans?" I asked.

"They won't care!" my father responded. "This isn't the first time I have
put down a threat to my rule ... and it probably won't be the last."

Then he looked at me and added, "Antipas, you have shown that you are
willing to do what must be done to rule this land. I will be changing the
terms of my will to remove Herod II as heir to the throne, and in his place
I will designate that you become the tetrarch of Galilee and Perea; your
brother, Archelaus, the ethnarch of Judea, Samaria, and Idumea; and your
half brother Philip the tetrarch of the lands north and east of the Jordan."

"Thank you, my father," I replied, "but it will be a very long time before
any of that comes about. You will continue to live a long and prosperous
life."

As Annas and I left the room, I said to him, "At least that is over and done
with. The threat has been averted. The Messiah is no more." But I could
tell Annas was not truly convinced. "Perhaps," he said, "perhaps."

. . .

Within a matter of days, my father became sick with an excruciatingly painful and festering illness. No one knew what kind of sickness it was or what had caused it. I asked Annas if he thought God was bringing His judgment on my father for the massacre of the children. "Perhaps," he again said, "perhaps."

My father traveled to the city of Jericho with its Roman baths and springs to convalesce from his illness. But his condition continued to worsen. He even attempted suicide to escape the pain he was in. Honestly, I do not know what the ultimate cause of his death was – his illness or a successful suicide attempt. What I do know is that his final wishes were honored. Caesar Augustus respected the terms of his will and divided the kingdom accordingly.

Annas and I never again spoke of the massacre of the children – nor did anyone else. The priests and the people continued to look to the stars and the horizon for their coming Messiah. And the years continued to pass.

I eventually divorced Phasaelis and married my true love, Herodias. But that's a story for another time.

Little did I know that one day – many years later – I would in fact come face-to-face with that child ...

∿

ALIM – THE MERCHANT

I am Alim, a merchant living in the city of Alexandria in the Roman province of Egypt. I still have difficulty referring to us as a province of the Roman empire. We were once the mightiest empire on the face of the earth, and now we are no more than a province of someone else's empire. But we know in our hearts from whence we came.

I was born when Cleopatra was our ruler. For almost twenty years she kept the Roman emperors at bay through her wiles and charms. That is until Augustus soundly defeated our forces, which were being led by her husband, Marc Antony. Our demise was sealed by the deaths of Cleopatra and Marc Antony in a tragic twist of fate as those two lovers took their own lives.

But life in Alexandria continued. We are the largest city in the world, rivaled only by Rome. We have transitioned from being the capital of our Egyptian empire to becoming a provincial capital of the Roman empire. We are situated on the trade route along the Mediterranean Sea that connects Europe with the eastern empires by land and by sea.

. . .

I followed in my father's footsteps as a merchant, and though I am not Jewish, my trading booth and home are located in the center of the delta quarter of our city. This quarter is heavily populated by Jews – the third largest people segment living in the city. I have been told that Alexandria has become the largest urban Jewish community in the world, surpassing Jerusalem.

We also are a world-renowned place of learning. As such, Alexandria has also become a leading center for rabbinical study for the Jews.

I trade primarily in grain, papyrus, and linen cloth. The papyrus is typically used for writing paper or to make twisted rope. The grain, of course, provides food and the cloth provides clothing. So, as a merchant, I help meet the needs of the families in our quarter. With our growing population, trade continues to be brisk, and there is great demand for my goods.

Two years ago, my oldest son, Khati, brought a Jewish man and his family to my trading booth. He had encountered them by the sea that morning. The man was looking to purchase a measure of grain. As we talked, I discovered that his name was Joseph and his wife's name was Mary. They had just arrived in the city. He was a carpenter looking for work, and they needed a place to stay.

Until recently, my cousin and his family had lived in a one-room home adjacent to mine. My cousin had unexpectedly moved to another part of the city, so I was looking for a tenant. I can usually find a new tenant quickly, but not this time. Perhaps it was intended for this family.

I also needed a good carpenter for several weeks' worth of work to make repairs for one of my business ventures. As I explained the stonework needed, Joseph told me he could easily do the work for me. We agreed on a trade – they would move into the home I had available in exchange for Joseph providing me with one week's work. That night, my new tenants settled into their home.

. . .

Joseph was a skilled carpenter. His work was far better than that of anyone else I had ever employed. And he completed the work in half the time I expected. I told some of my friends about him, and soon he was in great demand. I was grateful, because it assured me of having a stable tenant.

My wife, Nena, helped Mary become acclimated with the big city life of Alexandria, and the two women became fast friends. Our younger son was only a few months older than theirs, so our families seemed to be drawn together.

Eventually, Joseph confided in me that they had left Judea to protect their young son. They had learned of a plot by Herod the Great to massacre male children under two years of age who had been born in the area where Mary had given birth. He never told me how he learned of the plot, but his emphatic tone assured me he was serious. Though Egypt and Judea were both under the control of Caesar Augustus, King Herod's authority did not cross into our borders. So, Jesus was safe here.

Joseph said they began their journey from Jerusalem heading west toward the sea and soon intersected with the trade road that eventually led them here. He told me they hadn't set out for Alexandria initially. They knew they were coming to Egypt, but their God had directed them to our city as they made the journey.

He also told me a story of how the first patriarch of the Jewish people, Abraham, had come to Egypt over nineteen hundred years ago seeking refuge from a famine. Then Abraham's grandson had come to Egypt over seventeen hundred years ago also seeking refuge for his family from a famine. Now God had led Joseph to bring his family here to find refuge from a king who wanted to harm their son.

. . .

"Our God has used Egypt in an important way in the continuing story of our people – and now even my Son's story," Joseph said.

I was proud that our people had played such an important role in their story. But I also knew about the years our pharaohs had subjected the Jewish people to slavery. I knew the kindness I extended to Joseph and his family would never make up for the pain our pharaohs had caused his people – but perhaps it would be a small way for me to personally make amends.

We rarely spoke about our religious beliefs. My people in Alexandria pride ourselves on our acceptance and tolerance of differing beliefs. Nena and I believed in the gods of our ancestors – the gods of the sun and the moon, and the earth and the sea. We knew, on the other hand, that Joseph and Mary believed in one God, whom they called Jehovah. And the Jewish people believed that they were uniquely chosen to be the people of their God dating back to Abraham. We knew they had their rituals and practices, just as we did.

But things changed about a year ago. Mary confided something to Nena that forever changed our lives. She told Nena about their Son, Jesus, and how He came to be. She told how she had been a virgin when she conceived. She said an angel told her that the Spirit of God would come upon her and she would bear the Son of the Most High God.

In our religious beliefs, stories about one of our gods impregnating a woman were not that unusual, but we had never personally met a woman who told us she had been impregnated by God. It seemed even contrary to what the Jews believed. But Mary continued to explain how the angel had spoken to her cousin and also to Joseph. She told Nena about the shepherds who had heard an announcement from angels. And she told her about the Parthian magi who had followed a star to her doorstep.

. . .

She explained that an angel told Joseph to flee to Egypt to protect the child. And she told her how she and Joseph believed God had directed them to my trading booth that very first day.

One week later, we received word that the Herodian king had dispatched soldiers to massacre all the male children under two years of age in and around the town of Bethlehem. I could not believe that a king would do such a thing to the children of his own people. But then I remembered what Joseph told me about his reason for coming to Egypt – and Mary's words to Nena that an angel had warned them to escape Herod's wicked deed.

I thought about these things for a few weeks and then decided I needed to speak to Joseph.

"Joseph, I know you to be a man who fears your God and walks uprightly before Him. Nena and I have heard how your God has spoken to you and directed you – and how Jesus is His Son. I know you to be a man without guile. I believe that you believe what you have told us.

"But how is it that your God would choose a young virgin from a small town, betrothed to a poor carpenter, to give birth to His Son? Why wouldn't He choose a king and queen in a spectacular city like Alexandria or Jerusalem? Why would He allow His Son to be born in an animal stable and swaddled in a feeding trough instead of a palace? Why would He allow kings to attempt to harm His child when they should be worshipping Him?

"Why would His angels announce the birth to a group of shepherds instead of making the announcement to people of honor and position? Why would He lead Him to be raised in a single-room hovel on the backstreets of Alexandria?"

. . .

Joseph smiled and said, "Because that is what He said He would do. He said His Son would be born of a virgin.[(1)] He said His Son would be born in Bethlehem.[(2)] He said He would be worshipped by shepherds, and foreign kings would bring tributes to Him.[(3)] He said a king would slaughter children in an attempt to kill Him.[(4)] He said He would direct the child to Egypt.[(5)] He said He would raise a King from the line of David.[(6)] And He said so much more!

"He said His Son would grow up in humble surroundings.[(7)] And He said that He will become a Man of sorrows, despised, rejected, and acquainted with deepest grief on our behalf. He will carry our weaknesses and endure our punishment – not for His sins, but for ours.[(8)]

"Many years ago, Jehovah God provided a ram in a thicket to our patriarch Abraham to be offered as a sacrifice instead of his son Isaac. By faith Abraham believed that God would provide the sacrifice. He believed God will provide His own sacrifice on His mountain.[(9)] I believe that one day Jesus will be that sacrifice – the Lord will lay on Him the sins of us all.[(10)] That is what I believe, and that is why I believe.

"Alim, I don't know why God chose me to be the earthly father to His Son. I have never done anything to deserve it. But I know that He did choose me, and I will strive to be faithful to Him with every breath I take.

"And I don't know why He chose you to help us, but I know that He did. You, too, are a part of God's plan. Each of us has a part. God is at work in and through all of our lives that we might come to believe in Him and His Son. So, the question is no longer – why do I believe? The question now is – do you believe?

"When I didn't know, I asked God to show me. Are you willing – with an open heart and mind – to ask Him to show you?"

. . .

Joseph fell silent and humbly stared into my eyes. Then he turned and walked away. I was left with his questions echoing in my heart. I looked up toward the heavens and asked God to show me.

That night I told Nena all that Joseph had said. When I was done, I told her, "I believe." And she looked at me and said, "So do I." To our surprise, Khati – who had been listening in the other room – appeared and declared, "And so do I!"

The next morning, we went to Joseph and Mary to tell them we believe in their God ... and we believe in His Son! We asked them to help us know more about Him. From that day on, we were more than just friends, we were family.

So Nena, Khati, and I were saddened when several weeks later Joseph told me, "The angel of the Lord has again come to me and announced, *'Get up and take the Child and His mother back to the land of Israel. Those who were trying to kill Him are dead.'*"[11] It was time for them to go!

Joseph completed his work, and they packed up for their journey to Nazareth. Our hearts were heavy, but we knew they needed to return. We would miss them! But we knew we would see them again one day.

Little did I know where the path would lead them. Little did I know where the path would lead us. But for the first time in my life, when we bid them farewell, we knew Who was leading all of us ...

CLOPAS – THE UNCLE

*M*y name is Clopas. I am the son of Jacob the carpenter, and the younger brother of Joseph. I was born in Cana of Galilee and lived there for much of my life.

When I was sixteen years old, carpentry work was becoming difficult to find in Cana. My brother relocated to Nazareth while I remained in Cana with our father. Jehovah God continued to provide my father and me with enough work so we could keep food on our table.

When I was twenty-eight, I married a beautiful young woman named Mary. My brother and I must have similar tastes in women since our wives share the same name!

One year later, God blessed my wife and me with a son we named James. Even when he was young, we could tell he was going to be short-statured as an adult. Since he was shorter than other boys his age, he earned the nickname James the Less. But what he lacked in height, he more than made up for in brawn. He has always been a great helper to me in my work!

.   .   .

When James was five, we traveled to Nazareth to meet up with my brother Joseph so we could all travel together to Jerusalem for the Feast of the Passover. This was the first observance of Passover since our father died, so we all wanted to be together.

We were more than surprised to learn that Joseph was betrothed. We had met Mary and her father on previous visits to Nazareth, but we never imagined Joseph and Mary would marry because of their age difference. Though we were surprised, we also were grateful to hear the news. Joseph was filled with joy again – something that had been absent from his life since his wife, Rebekah, died.

Mary was currently in Hebron so her father, Eli, would be joining us in our travels to Jerusalem. Even though I missed our father's company as we made the journey, Joseph's glee helped to lighten my heart. I enjoyed watching the brother-like relationship that had developed between Joseph and his future father-in-law. Their friendship had obviously deepened.

We enjoyed our time in Jerusalem and had even briefly visited our cousin, Achim. Our time together passed quickly, and we all looked forward to coming back together again in December for Joseph and Mary's marriage feast in Nazareth.

So imagine my surprise when in early May, just a few months later, Joseph and Mary paid us an unexpected visit in Cana. It had been over a year since I had last seen Mary, so nothing appeared unusual. I welcomed them into our home and invited them to sit down and rest from their travels as my Mary prepared refreshments.

After my wife rejoined us, Joseph explained that he and Mary had news to tell us. I looked over at my wife and she appeared to already know what this might be about.

. . .

"Soon after we announced our betrothal," Joseph began, "an angel of the Lord came to Mary and told her that Jehovah God had chosen her, and the Spirit of God would come over her and she would conceive a child. The child will be the Son of the Most High God. He is the Messiah – whose coming the prophets foretold.

"Isaiah wrote that the Messiah would be born of a virgin – and now God has chosen Mary to be that virgin. Mary told her father and me about the angel's visit after she returned from Hebron last month. By that time, she had been pregnant for three months.

"The messenger of God confirmed the message through Mary's cousins, Zechariah and Elizabeth, and he has confirmed it to me through a dream. We know that she is the most blessed of women – but we also know how this has appeared to our neighbors. The angel confirmed that I should bring her into my home as my wife. And I have done so. However, we will not consummate our marriage until after the child is born.

"You are my closest family, so we wanted you to know and understand as soon as possible. We know how shocking this all sounds. We both have experienced that shock firsthand ourselves. So, feel free to ask us any questions you might have."

I know my brother – and I know him to be an upright man of integrity. I know that he loves God and strives to stand righteous before Him. I know that my brother will not lie about his own actions or anyone else's. His word was all I needed to hear to know that what he told us was the truth.

So, I looked at my brother and his wife and said, "We join together with you in praising Jehovah God for His faithfulness in sending His Messiah, for His mercy in allowing us to now sit here in the baby's presence, and for His grace in the way He is enabling you to walk through this with Him. Mary, you truly are blessed by God above all other women. And

Joseph, our God has chosen well to choose you to be the earthly father to His Son."

We all embraced and spent the remainder of our time together rejoicing and praising God. Two days later, Joseph and Mary returned to Nazareth. As the days went by, my wife and I knew our lives would be different in light of this news. We were to be an uncle and aunt to the Messiah. Our son, James, would be His cousin. How could we have ever supposed that God would allow an unknown family like us to bear witness to His Son in such a way? He is indeed a merciful and gracious God!

My wife and I are both of the tribe of Judah and the line of David. So, when Caesar decreed that every person needed to return to their ancestral home for the census, that meant we must return to Bethlehem. My wife's sister and her husband live in Bethlehem, so we knew we would be expected to stay with them.

We also knew that Joseph, Mary, and Eli would be making the same journey. And we knew that the baby would soon arrive. We made arrangements to meet up with them in Nazareth and travel to Bethlehem together so we could be of help. When we arrived in Nazareth, we learned that Eli was ill and would not be making the trip. Gratefully, there were others remaining in the town who would care for him. So, the rest of us set out on the journey.

When we arrived in Bethlehem, we parted ways. Joseph and Mary went on to our cousin Achim's home, while my wife and I continued on to my sister-in-law's home. We were grateful for their hospitality. Their home was small, and other relatives had also come, so we made the best of the tight sleeping quarters and enjoyed the fellowship.

The next morning, Joseph came to my sister-in-law's home to see me. He told me the baby had been born the night before. He said a group of angels had announced the birth to shepherds in the hills. He told me how they had come to worship the child. He was in awe of all that had occurred.

But he also told me that Achim had not taken the news of the baby well. Joseph and Mary had spent the night in the stable, but this morning Achim had agreed to allow Mary and the baby to stay in the house until her time of purification was complete.

"However," Joseph said, "I am not welcome in their home. This morning I went to the synagogue and registered for the census. Now I am headed to Jerusalem to find work for the next few weeks until Mary's time is completed."

"Brother, I am so sorry that Achim has treated you this way," I replied. "I would see if you could stay here in this home, but I know they have no room."

"I know that Jehovah God has a divine plan in all of this," Joseph responded. "So we will trust Him that He will use this to further His purpose in everyone's lives."

Joseph asked if we would go through Nazareth and check on Eli when we returned home. I told him we would. As we began our journey home, Mary and I talked about the way Joseph and his wife were being treated by family and by their neighbors. We decided we needed to move to Nazareth to help them and encourage them. There was really nothing to keep us in Cana any longer. We knew it was what God would have us do.

When we arrived in Nazareth, Eli was disheartened that Joseph and Mary would be delayed in their return, but he rejoiced in the news of the baby's birth. I told him the baby's name was Jesus. He was delighted to hear it and also seemed genuinely pleased about our decision to move to Nazareth. I realized we were not moving here to only encourage Joseph and Mary, we would also be encouraging Eli.

· · ·

I traveled to Cana while Mary and James remained in Nazareth. I settled our affairs, gathered our few belongings, and brought them to Nazareth. While we waited for Joseph, Mary, and Jesus, we stayed in their home.

Two months later, we received a message from Joseph that an angel of the Lord had directed them to go to Egypt. They did not know when they would return. He asked that we continue to care for Eli. They did not know of our decision to permanently move here – but we marveled at the goodness of God as He ordered all of our steps!

Eli never fully recovered from his fever. As time went on, his health continued to decline and he died. The day before he took his last breath, he told me how grateful he was to God for all of His many blessings:

- a wife he had loved with all of his heart
- a daughter he knew God would always watch over
- a grandchild – the Messiah – whom he would not meet now, but he would meet in heaven
- a son-in-law who was not only a good friend but a righteous man
- for me and my family and our time together those last few weeks.

It was a few years before Joseph and Mary returned to Nazareth. We had moved into Eli's home at his insistence, and I had been able to carry on with Eli and Joseph's carpentry trade in their absence. James was now becoming more of a help to me in the trade. And two years ago, God had blessed us with a second son, Thaddeus!

For the next several years, we enjoyed sharing life together with Joseph and his family. God blessed us all bountifully! Joseph fathered four sons – James, young Joseph, Jude, and Simon – and two daughters. Jesus was the model oldest son and an attentive big brother. He grew – not only in height, but also in wisdom and maturity.

· · ·

When Jesus was twelve, we all traveled to Jerusalem together for the Passover festival. Several other families from our town made the trip with us. Over the years, the neighbors' disdain toward Joseph and Mary had subsided. So, trips to Jerusalem were a break for everyone from their daily routine and a chance for camaraderie and fun. The men and women traveled in their separate groups and the older children did the same. It was possible to go for days without seeing an older child because he was off with the others.

When we stopped for the night on our journey back home, Joseph and Mary discovered that Jesus was missing. Mary had been busy watching over their six younger children, who ranged in ages from two to nine. She assumed Jesus had gone on ahead with the older children.

But now Joseph and Mary could not find Him anywhere. After checking with everyone, they decided to return to Jerusalem. Seeing how distraught they were, I decided to join them in the search. My wife agreed to take their other children, together with our children, and continue the journey home with the rest of our party.

For three days we searched for Jesus all over the city. But on the fourth, we decided to go to the temple. There we found Jesus sitting among the rabbis, discussing deep doctrinal truths. When we saw Him, His back was to us. But we could see the look of amazement on the faces of those sitting around Him. He spoke in a way that astounded them – and not just because He was so young.

Finally, Mary interrupted Him and said, *"Why have you done this to us? Your father and I have been frantic searching for You everywhere."*[1]

Jesus stood up and looked at her compassionately and respectfully as He said, *"Why did you need to search? You should have known that I would be in My Father's house."*[2]

. . .

I don't believe any of us fully grasped the implications of His answer. And it was not the last time He gave us cause to consider the greater meaning of His words. We became more and more mindful that Jesus was not just any young man. He is the Son of God.

Joseph and I, together with all of our sons, worked as carpenters for another eight years – until my brother died. Jesus then carried on as the head of His home and as the patriarch of His family for another eight years. He worked hard – but He was also known to play hard. As the years went by, I realized I was no longer viewing Him as my nephew – I was viewing Him as my Master. And then one day, He announced to all of us that His time was near.

Little did I know what that meant. Little did I know the journey that was before Him. Little did I know where it would lead. But I always knew, wherever the journey led, I would follow …

∾

JAMES – THE BROTHER

I am James, the son of Joseph and Mary. I was born in the town of Nazareth soon after my parents returned from Egypt. Jesus and I share the same mother, so we are referred to as half brothers. My father may not be Jesus's natural father, but my father sure acts like he is.

For the first few years of my life, I had no idea that Jesus and I had different fathers. All I knew was that I had a big brother who was three years older – and we had a father who treated us both the same.

As the years passed, we became a family of nine – our parents, five boys, and two girls. After Jesus and me, there was young Joseph, Jude, and Simon. Our two sisters were the youngest. Jesus was almost ten years older than our youngest sister.

Each time our family grew, so did our humble home. Our father found a way to add a little space here and there. The five boys slept in one slightly enlarged room. Our sisters had a much smaller room. And our parents had another small room for themselves.

. . .

Before I tell you anything else, you need to know that Jesus was a great older brother! From a young age, all the boys helped our father with his carpentry work. He took great pride in his work – and he took great pride in teaching all of us how to be skilled craftsmen. He helped each son make his own tools. And he made us responsible for helping to train our younger brother, which meant Jesus helped train me.

Our father showed Jesus how to make toy models of animals when I was about three years old. Jesus made a set of animals for me together with a small wooden ark. I would repeat the story of Noah and the flood over and over again as I played with the ark and the animals. When I was a little older, Jesus made dolls for me representing David and Goliath. They became two of my most prized possessions as I told the story of how our ancestor King David defeated the Philistine giant.

Jesus and I also played together with a ball made out of an animal skin stuffed with husks. We enjoyed kicking the ball back and forth to each other and began to assign scores for the farthest or most difficult kicks. Then as we got older, our games advanced, as well.

Jesus was always stronger than I was. We tested our strength by lifting stones. We used heavy round stones of varying weights and challenged each other whether we could lift them to our knees, our waists, our shoulders, or above our heads.

Though Jesus always outlifted me, I learned early on I could outrun Him. We loved to race each other and continued that sport well into our early adulthood – though finding time to run together became increasingly difficult.

I wasn't very old when I learned that Jesus's greatest passion was reading and studying the Scriptures. Early in the morning and after the end of the workday, Jesus could often be found at the synagogue reading the Scriptures, listening to teachings, and discussing truths with the rabbis. He instilled within me, as well as all of our brothers, a thirst for the Scriptures. Of all of our brothers, that was particularly true of our next to youngest brother, Jude.

I never observed Jesus utter a harsh word or disrespect anyone, whether it was our parents, our teachers, our neighbors, adults, or children. He showed compassion for everyone He met. He seemed incapable of sinning. I, however, had a knack for getting into trouble – despite my best intentions. No matter how hard I tried as I got older, I would find myself doing something I wasn't supposed to do, or not doing something I was supposed to do. But Jesus never did.

I'll never forget the time our entire family went to Jerusalem to celebrate the Passover Feast. I was ten and Jesus was twelve. The day after we arrived, our family went to the temple to offer our sacrifice to the Lord. As we continued to pray, my mother and sisters went to the court of women and my father and the boys went to the men's court.

After a while, I saw Jesus walk over to where the rabbis were teaching. He sat down and joined them. I soon walked over to sit with Him. Before long, He was participating in the conversation – asking questions, giving answers, and quoting Scriptures. I couldn't imagine myself speaking up, at my age or His. And apparently some of the men were questioning His right to speak. But soon His knowledge of the Scriptures silenced even His most outspoken critics. I, too, marveled at my brother.

We remained in Jerusalem for a few more days – and each day Jesus slipped off to the temple to engage in conversation. I was able to join Him twice more. Each time I noticed that more people were coming just to see the young boy who was speaking with an authority that challenged – or even overshadowed – that of the religious leaders.

The next day, we departed for home. That evening my mother asked me if I knew where Jesus was. I still had to travel within eyesight of my mother. I couldn't wait for one more year to pass so I could join Jesus and the other older boys. He had walked with them on our way to Jerusalem, so my parents thought He was with them today. But none of the boys had seen Him.

This was unusual for Jesus. He never did anything close to disobeying our parents! No one could imagine what had happened to Him. My parents were worried and decided to return to Jerusalem to find Him. My uncle Clopas joined them in their search. The rest of my siblings and I continued our journey home under the charge of my aunt Mary. My father instructed me to help my aunt watch out for the rest of my brothers and sisters. This was the first time he had given me the responsibility of being the big brother – and I was very proud.

My parents, uncle, and Jesus arrived at our home a few days after we did. My parents explained to our family, as well as all of our neighbors, that they found Jesus with the teachers in the temple. I wasn't surprised. It all seemed very natural.

Soon afterward, my parents explained to me who Jesus is. They told me He had remained at the temple to be in His Father's house about His Father's business.[1] They told me the story of how He had come to be born. They explained that though my father was Jesus's earthly father, He is in fact the Son of God. For ten years, I had looked at Him as my big brother. Now I was being told He was God's Son.

A lot of things made sense after that revelation. His teaching and understanding of Scriptures for one, and His sinless behavior for another. But it also caused me to look at Him much differently – and somehow, I knew our relationship would never be the same.

I am ashamed to admit I became jealous of Jesus. How could I ever measure up to a brother who is the Son of God? I was afraid I would be seen as inferior in the eyes of my mother and father. No angels announced my birth! And no wise men from distant lands brought gifts to herald my arrival!

. . .

As jealousy took root, so did anger and bitterness. If Jesus was the Son of God, why did we live in such humble surroundings? Why didn't we live in a palace, lavished with the riches of this world? Why does our father have to work so hard to earn a living to provide for us?

Then a few years later when our father fell ill and died, I found myself asking, "Jesus, if You are the Son of God, why did You not heal our father? He gave everything for You. He loved You like a son. He protected You. He provided for You. Why did You not keep him from dying?"

I'm not sure which words I actually spoke out loud to Jesus and which I just said to myself. But I became bitter toward Him. By the time our father died, all of my siblings also knew the truth about Jesus – and they had some of the same questions.

Although my mother was grieving my father's death, she did not seem to harbor the same questions or resentment toward Jesus. As a matter of fact, she sought His comfort. Jesus, too, was grieving our father's death – but He told all of us that our father was now in paradise. He no longer had any pain. He was resting in the bosom of Abraham. And one day very soon, he would enter into his reward.

Jesus told us that He had come so all of us might have eternal life. He knew our father had trusted by faith. Jesus told us that He, too, missed him. He missed having our father to talk to, to laugh with, to weep with, to walk with, and to work with. I knew, and it was obvious, Jesus loved our father.

Jesus told us that one day He will forever hold the keys of death and eternity. On that day, He will lead those who have died before His sacrifice into the heavenly kingdom. And He told us that on that day, as He leads that procession, our father will be right by His side with that multitude.

· · ·

I wanted to believe. I wanted to find the solace my mother had found. I wanted to have the hope my brothers and sisters were beginning to feel. But it wasn't there. And all Jesus would say was that it was not yet His time. So, we buried our father, and life continued – but it was different.

As the oldest Son, Jesus stepped into the role as the patriarch of our family. He assumed the role of partner with our uncle Clopas and became the lead carpenter. Our family and my uncle and his sons all continued to work together, providing for our mother and our families. Though the pain of the loss of my father diminished, it was never erased from my heart. My doubt, my bitterness, and my lack of faith continued.

Eight years after our father's death, Jesus announced that His time would soon arrive. In the meantime, He would need to be about His Father's business. He directed me to assume leadership of the family carpentry trade. I would now step into a role for which I had been groomed and well-equipped – the role of Joseph's eldest son.

As I think back on the day Jesus left our home, and left the bedroom that He and I had shared all of our lives, I realized that despite my feelings toward Him, Jesus placed great trust in me. He had been my big brother and my mentor. He had always encouraged me and loved me. He was always cheering me on. Until the day He left, He was always there for me.

For the next three years, Jesus traveled throughout the countryside, from city to city. Our mother traveled with Him most of the time. He healed the sick. He made the blind to see and the lame to walk. He raised the dead to life. But each time I heard about His miracles, I thought of my father and why He had allowed him to die.

Jesus preached the Good News of the kingdom to everyone who would listen, and many did. But, I did not!

.   .   .

One day during Passover a few years later, I was in Jerusalem when I heard that Jesus had been arrested – and placed on a cross to die. I knew my mother and a few of His followers were gathered there at the cross. I knew that I should be there. Jesus was my older brother! But the bitterness in my heart wouldn't allow me to go. Some people thought I stayed away for fear of my own life, but nothing could be further from the truth. I stayed away because He had not healed our father.

Jesus died that day. And I learned He had asked His disciple John to care for our mother. It should have been me He charged with that responsibility. But I wasn't at the foot of the cross – John was.

I couldn't even seek out my mother to grieve with her and console her. I heard she was in Bethany at the home of some of His friends and followers. I would leave it to them to console her.

But on the third day, I received news that Jesus had risen from the grave! My uncle Clopas sought me out to tell me that Jesus was alive and to convey this message:

"Jesus told me to tell you, 'I now hold the keys of death and eternity. The captives have been set free! And I have walked with the multitude from paradise through the gates of heaven!(2) And our father was right by My side! Your father is more alive today than he has ever been. And he, and I, both want you to have hope!'"

At that moment, all the bitterness and anger I had kept inside me washed away. I laid my head on my uncle's neck and wept. But I no longer wept out of sorrow. I wept because I knew I had been set free. My father had never been captive or lost. I was the one who had been captive. I was a prisoner to my jealousy and my bitterness. Jesus had set me free! He had paid the price for my sins and He had forgiven me!

. . .

I joined my uncle and looked for my mother, who was gathered together with Jesus's followers. Later that night, He appeared to all of us. There He stood – my Savior, my Lord, and my brother!

Little did I know what all He had done. Little did I fully comprehend it. Little did I know what was in store for me in the days ahead. But I knew the little baby in the manger had now completed His work as the Savior of the world!

❦

PLEASE HELP ME BY LEAVING A REVIEW!

≈

i would be very grateful if you would leave a review of this book. Your feedback will be helpful to me in my future writing endeavors and will also assist others as they consider picking up a copy of the book.

To leave a review:

Go to *amazon.com/dp/1734193042*

Or scan this QR code using your camera on your smartphone:

Thanks for your help!

≈

THE STORY CONTINUES ...

Not Too Little To Know

THE EYEWITNESSES COLLECTION BOOK #2

Experience the Advent through the eyes of ten
children who witnessed the glorious arrival of the
Promised One. Join Isaac, Salome, Sarah, Yanzu and
others in their journeys as they share their own
fictional eyewitness accounts of the prophecies and
events surrounding the birth of Jesus. **Some of the
characters may be fictional, but the truth they tell
is very real!**

This illustrated chapter book has been written for
ages 8 and up. It is a companion to **Little Did We Know**, a collection of short stories
written for teens and adults. Though both books stand alone, their stories
intertwine into a delightful Advent journey for the entire family.

Exclusively available through Amazon.

IF YOU ENJOYED THIS BOOK ...

... you will want to read the rest of "The Eyewitnesses" Collection

The first four books in these collections of short stories chronicle the first person eyewitness accounts of eighty-five men, women and children and their unique relationships with Jesus.

Little Did We Know – the advent of Jesus (Book 1)

Not Too Little To Know – the advent – ages 8 thru adult (Book 2)

The One Who Stood Before Us – the ministry and passion of Jesus (Book 3)

The Little Ones Who Came – the ministry and passion – ages 8 thru adult (Book 4)

The Patriarchs — eyewitnesses from the beginning — Adam through Moses tell their stories (Book 5) — releasing in 2023

Now available through Amazon.

Scan this QR code using your camera on your smartphone to see the entire collection on Amazon:

~

INTRODUCING MY NEWEST SERIES

You will want to read all of the books in "The Called" series

Experience the stories of these ordinary men and women who were called by God to be used in extraordinary ways through this series of first-person biblical fiction novellas.

A Carpenter Called Joseph (Book 1)

A Prophet Called Isaiah (Book 2)

A Teacher Called Nicodemus (Book 3)

A Judge Called Deborah (Book 4) - releasing May 20

A Merchant Called Lydia (Book 5) - releasing July 22, 2022

A Friend Called Enoch (Book 6) - releasing Fall 2022

Available through Amazon.

Scan this QR code using your camera on your smartphone to see the entire series on Amazon:

THROUGH THE EYES SERIES

... the other books in the *"THROUGH THE EYES"* SERIES

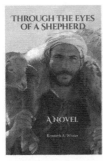  

Experience the truths of Scripture as these stories unfold through the lives and eyes of a shepherd, a spy and a prisoner. Rooted in biblical truth, these fictional novels will enable you to draw beside the storytellers as they worship the Baby in the manger, the Son who took up the cross, the Savior who conquered the grave, the Deliverer who parted the sea and the Eternal God who has always had a mission.

Through the Eyes of a Shepherd (Book 1)

Through the Eyes of a Spy (Book 2)

Through the Eyes of a Prisoner (Book 3)

Now available through Amazon.

Scan this QR code using your camera on your smartphone to see the entire series on Amazon:

∽

LESSONS LEARNED IN THE WILDERNESS SERIES

The Lessons Learned In The Wilderness series

A non-fiction series of devotional studies

There are lessons that can only be learned in the wilderness experiences of our lives. As we see throughout the Bible, God is right there leading us each and every step of the way, if we will follow Him. Wherever we are, whatever we are experiencing, He will use it to enable us to experience His Person, witness His power and join Him in His mission.

The Journey Begins (Exodus) – Book 1

The Wandering Years (Numbers and Deuteronomy) – Book 2

Possessing The Promise (Joshua and Judges) – Book 3

Walking With The Master (The Gospels leading up to Palm Sunday) – Book 4

Taking Up The Cross (The Gospels – the passion through ascension) – Book 5

Until He Returns (The Book of Acts) – Book 6

The complete series is also available in two e-book boxsets or two single soft-cover print volumes.

Now available through Amazon.

Scan this QR code using your camera on your smartphone to see the entire series on Amazon:

———————-

For more information, go to:

wildernesslessons.com or kenwinter.org

ALSO AVAILABLE AS AN AUDIOBOOK

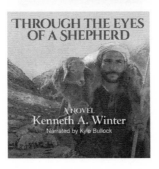

SCRIPTURE BIBLIOGRAPHY

~

Much of the storyline of this book is taken from the Gospels according to Matthew and Luke, as well as the history and prophesies of the Old Testament. Certain fictional events or depictions of those events have been added.

Specific references and quotations:

Chapter 2

[1] Genesis 6:5-18

[2] Genesis 9:8-17

[3] Genesis 12:1-3 (ESV)

[4] Genesis 12:11-13 (ESV)

[5] Genesis 13:14-17 (ESV)

[6] Genesis 16:2 (ESV)

[7] Genesis 17:5-8 (ESV)

[8] Genesis 17:9-14 - paraphrase

[9] Genesis 17:15-16 (ESV)

(10)Genesis 17:21 - paraphrase

(11)Genesis 21:13 (ESV)

(12)Genesis 22:2 (ESV)

(13)Genesis 22:7 (ESV)

(14)Genesis 22:8 (ESV)

(15)Genesis 22:11-12 (ESV)

(16)Genesis 22:16-18 (ESV)

Chapter 3

(1) 1 Samuel 17:26 (ESV)

(2) 1 Samuel 17:37 (ESV)

(3) 1 Samuel 24:11-12 paraphrase

(4) 1 Samuel 24:17, 20 (ESV)

(5) 2 Samuel 6:6-16 (ESV)

(6) Psalm 110:1-7 (ESV)

Chapter 4

(1) 2 Kings 20:1

(2) 2 Kings 20:5-6

(3) Joshua 10:12-13

(4) Isaiah 14:26-27

(5) Isaiah 53:1-6

(6) Isaiah 9:6-7

(7) Isaiah 7:14

(8) Isaiah 35:5-6

Chapter 5

(1) Nehemiah 8:6

(2) Malachi 3:8-9

(3) Malachi 2:14-16

(4) Malachi 3:13-14

(5) Malachi 4:1-2

(6) Malachi 4:6

Chapter 6

(1) Luke 1:19

(2) Daniel 10:21

(3) Genesis 18:1-15

(4) Genesis 18:14

(5) Genesis 18:16-33

(6) Genesis 19:1-29

(7) Daniel 8:18-26; 9:21-27; 10:10-12:4

(8) Luke 1:13-17

(9) Luke 1:18

(10)Luke 1:19

(11)Luke 1:28

(12)Luke 1:30-33

(13)Luke 1:34

(14)Luke 1:35

(15)Luke 1:36-37

(16)Luke 1:38

(17)Matthew 1:20

(18)Luke 2:14

Chapter 7

(1) Luke 1:13

(2) Luke 1:18

(3) Luke 1:19-20

(4) Luke 1:17

Chapter 8

(1) Luke 1:28

(2) Luke 1:30

(3) Luke 1:30-32

(4) Luke 1:34

(5) Luke 1:35

(6) Luke 1:36-37

(7) Luke 1:38

(8) Luke 1:42-43

(9) Luke 1:44-45

(10) Luke 1:46-49, 54-55

Chapter 9

(1) Psalm 127:3

(2) Luke 1:25

(3) Luke 1:42

(4) Luke 1:43-44

(5) Luke 1:36-37

(6) Luke 1:45

(7) Luke 1:46-48, 55

(8) Luke 1:60

(9) Luke 1:61

(10) Luke 1:63

(11) Luke 1:66

(12) Luke 1:78-79

Chapter 10

[1] Isaiah 7:14 (ESV)

Chapter 11

[1] Luke 1:30-33

[2] Matthew 1:20-23

Chapter 12

[1] Luke 1:30-32, 35

[2] Matthew 1:23

Chapter 13

[1] Psalm 127:3, 5

Chapter 14

[1] Luke 2:10-11

[2] Luke 2:14

[3] Luke 2:15

Chapter 15

[1] Exodus 20:14

Chapter 16

[1] Matthew 2:2 (ESV)

[2] Matthew 2:8 (ESV)

Chapter 17

[1] Exodus 20:14

Chapter 18

[1] Micah 5:2

Chapter 19

[1]Matthew 2:2 (ESV)

[2]Matthew 2:5-6 (ESV)

[3]Matthew 2:8 (ESV)

Chapter 20

[1]Isaiah 9:6-7 (ESV)

[2]Leviticus 12

[3]Exodus 13:1-12

[4]Luke 2:34-35 (ESV)

[5]Luke 2:29-32 (ESV)

Chapter 21

[1]Jeremiah 29:11 (NIV)

[2]Matthew 2:13 (ESV)

Chapter 23

[1] Isaiah 7:14

[2] Micah 5:2

[3] Psalm 72:9-10

[4] Jeremiah 31:15

[5] Hosea 11:1

[6] Jeremiah 23:5-6

[7] Isaiah 53:2

[8] Isaiah 53:3-6

[9] Genesis 22:8-14

[10]Isaiah 53:6

[11]Matthew 2:20

Chapter 24

[1] Luke 2:48

(2) Luke 2:49

Chapter 25

(1) Luke 2:49

(2) Revelation 1:18; Ephesians 4:8-10

Unless otherwise indicated, all Scripture quotations are taken from the Holy Bible, New Living Translation, copyright © 1996. Used by permission of Tyndale House Publishers, Inc., Wheaton, Illinois 60189. All rights reserved.

Scripture quotations marked (ESV) are taken from The Holy Bible, English Standard Version, copyright © 2001 by Crossway, a publishing ministry of Good News Publishers. Used by permission. All rights reserved.

Scripture quotations marked (NIV) are taken from The Holy Bible, New International Version® NIV® Copyright © 1973, 1978, 1984, 2011 by Biblica, Inc. TM Used by permission. All rights reserved worldwide.

∼

LISTING OF CHARACTERS

~

Many of the characters in this book are real people pulled directly from the pages of Scripture — most notably Jesus! i have not changed any details about a number of those individuals —again, most notably Jesus — except the addition of their interactions with the fictional characters. They are noted below as "UN" (unchanged).

In other instances, fictional details have been added to real people to provide backgrounds about their lives where Scripture is silent. The intent is that you understand these were real people, whose lives were full of all of the many details that fill our own lives. They had a history before they met Jesus ... and they had a future after they met Him. They are noted as "FB" (fictional background).

In some instances, we are never told the names of certain individuals in the Bible. In those instances, where i have given them a name as well as a fictional background, they are noted as "FN" (fictional name).

Lastly, a number of the characters are purely fictional, added to convey the fictional elements of these stories . They are noted as "FC" (fictional character).

∾

Jesus – the Son of God (UN)

The storyteller and his friends:

Luke - the physician (FB)

Saul/ Paul - the apostle (UN)

Theophilus - friend of Luke/ governor of Antioch (UN)

The patriarchs and their family members:

Abram/Abraham - the patriarch (FB)

Isaac - son of Abraham (UN)

Adam – the patriarch (UN)

Eve – wife of Adam (UN)

Noah – the patriarch (UN)

Shem – eldest son of Noah (UN)

Terah - father of Abraham (FB)

Sarai/ Sarah – wife of Abraham (FB)

Lot – nephew of Abraham (UN)

Esau – son of Isaac (UN)

Jacob/ Israel – son of Isaac (UN)

Joseph – son of Jacob (UN)

The kings, the prophets and their family members:

David - the shepherd/ second king of Israel (UN)

Jesse - father of David (UN)

Boaz - great grandfather of David (UN)

Ruth – wife of Boaz (UN)

Samuel - the last judge/ prophet (UN)

Saul - first king of Israel (UN)

Goliath - the Philistine giant (UN)

Jonathan - son of Saul (UN)

Merab - oldest daughter of Saul (UN)

Michal - second daughter of Saul (UN)

Abner - commander of King Saul's army (UN)

Ish-bosheth - son of King Saul (UN)

Nathan - the prophet who followed Samuel (UN)

King Solomon - son of David/ third king of Israel (UN)

Isaiah - the prophet (FB)

Amoz - father of Isaiah/ son of King Joash (UN)

King Joash - grandfather of Isaiah/ king of Judah (UN)

King Amaziah - son of Joash/ uncle of Isaiah (UN)

King Uzziah - son of Amaziah/ cousin of Isaiah (UN)

King Jotham - son of Uzziah/ 2nd cousin of Isaiah (UN)

King Ahaz - son of Jotham/ 3rd cousin of Isaiah (UN)

King Hezekiah - son of Ahaz/ son-in-law of Isaiah (FB)

King Manasseh - son of Hezekiah/ grandson of Isaiah (FB)

The prophets, the governors and the rulers during the years of captivity:

Malachi - the messenger (FB)

Zerubbabel - the governor sent to restore Jerusalem/ grandson of Jeconiah (UN)

Ezra - the priest sent to restore the temple in Jerusalem (UN)

Nehemiah - the governor sent to rebuild the walls and restore the city (UN)

King Nebuchadnezzar - king of Babylon (UN)

King Cyrus the Great - king of Persia (UN)

King Darius - king of Persia (UN)

King Xerxes - king of Persia (UN)

Hadassah/ Queen Esther - wife of Xerxes (FB)

Haman -- Agagite prime minister of Persia under Xerxes (FB)

Mordecai - Hebrew prime minister of Persia under Xerxes (FB)

King Artaxerxes - king of Persia, son of Xerxes (FB)

Daniel – prophet in captivity to Nebuchadnezzar and Darius (UN)

The angels:

Gabriel - a messenger from God (UN)

Michael - the archangel (UN)

The baptizer and his family members:

John the baptizer (FB)

Zechariah - the priest/ father of John the baptizer (FB)

Elizabeth - wife of Zechariah/ mother of John the baptizer (FB)

Abdiel - the Levite priest/ father of Zechariah (FC)

Menachem - priest/ older brother of Zechariah/ husband of Anna (FC)

Anna - wife of Menachem/ prophetess (FB)

Phanuel the Asherite - father of Anna (FC)

Adriel - son of Elizabeth's brother/ guardian of John the baptizer (FC)

Unnamed older brother of Elizabeth - father of Adriel (FC)

Joanna - wife of Adriel (FC)

The Maccabean leader:

Judas Maccabeus - priest that led Jewish people in revolt (UN)

Joseph, Mary and their family members:

Joseph - husband of Mary - earthly father of Jesus (FB)

Jacob - father of Joseph (FB)

Matthan - grandfather of Joseph (FB)

Eliud - great, great grandfather of Joseph (FB)

Rebekah - first wife of Joseph (FC)

Mary - mother of Jesus/ wife of Joseph (FB)

Matthat - grandfather of Mary (FB)

Unnamed grandmother of Mary/ Elizabeth's father's sister (FB)

Eli - father of Mary (FB)

Abigail - wife of Eli/ mother of Mary (FC)

James - brother of Jesus (FB)

Joseph - brother of Jesus (UN)

Jude - brother of Jesus (FB)

Simon - brother of Jesus (UN)

Mary - daughter of Joseph and Mary (FN)

Salome - daughter of Joseph and Mary (FN)

Clopas - brother of Joseph/ uncle of Jesus (FB)

Mary - wife of Clopas (FB)

James - son of Clopas (FB)

Thaddeus - son of Clopas (FB)

Jacob - father of Joseph and Clopas (FB)

The rabbi in Nazareth:

Jacob - elder and rabbi in Nazareth (FC)

Joazar - father of Jacob the rabbi (FC)

Those who encountered Jesus as a baby, and their family members:

Moshe - the shepherd (FC)

Ayda – wife of Moshe/ mother of Shimon (FC)

Shimon – eldest son of Moshe (FC)

Jacob – second son of Moshe (FC)

Eliezer - youngest son of Moshe (FC)

Achim - cousin of Joseph/ in Bethlehem (FC)

Miriam - wife of Achim/ in Bethlehem (FC)

Eliezer - son of Achim/ in Bethlehem (FC)

Tamar - wife of Eliezer/ in Bethlehem (FC)

Daniel - infant son of Eliezer/ in Bethlehem (FC)

Sarah - granddaughter of Achim/ in Bethlehem (FC)

Balthazar - the Parthian scholar (FC)

Unnamed father of Balthazar - governor of province (FC)

Unnamed brother of Balthazar - governor of province (FC)

Yanzu - servant of Balthazar (FC)

Levi - chief rabbi in Bethlehem (FC)

Simeon - the ancient who God promised would see the Messiah (FB)

Ashriel - great grandson of Simeon (FC)

Alim - the Egyptian merchant (FC)

Nena - wife of Alim (FC)

Khati - oldest son of Alim (FC)

Unnamed younger son of Alim (FC)

Salome - childhood friend of Mary (FC)

The religious leaders:

Hillel - the elder (FB)

Gamaliel - grandson of Hillel (FB)

John Hyrcanus II - Hasmonean high priest (76 - 66 BC) (UN)

Eleazar ben Boethus - Hasmonean high priest (4 - 3 BC) (UN)

Annas - high priest (6 – 15 AD) (FB)

Seth - father of Annas/ member of Sanhedrin (UN)

The Herodians and their family members:

Herod the Great – the tetrarch (UN)

Malthace – 4th wife of Herod/ mother of Antipas (UN)

Herod Antipas - 6th son (ruled 2 BC - 39 AD) (FB)

Phasaelis - princess of Nabataea/ first wife of Antipas (UN)

Herodias - divorced Herod II/ second wife of Antipas (UN)

Salome - daughter of Herodias & Herod II (UN)

Herod II – 4th son (UN)

Herod Archelaus - 5th son (ruled 2 BC - 6 AD) (UN)

Herod Philip II - 7th son (ruled 2 BC - 34 AD) (UN)

The Roman Emperor:

Caesar Augustus (27 BC – 14 AD) (UN)

~

ACKNOWLEDGMENTS

I do not cease to give thanks for you ....
Ephesians 1:16 (ESV)

∿

With a grateful heart:
to my wife, life partner and best friend, LaVonne,
for faithfully trusting God throughout every step
of our faith adventure together;

to my family,
for your constant encouragement;

to Sheryl,
for helping me tell the stories of the advent of Jesus
in a much better way;

to Dennis,
for taking an idea and making it a reality in such a beautiful way;

to Kyle and Devon,
for bringing all of the characters in this book alive in the audiobook
version;

and most importantly,
to the One without whom there would be no story
– our Lord and Savior Jesus Christ –
because the advent would have no meaning without the cross,
and the cross would have no meaning without the empty tomb.

ABOUT THE AUTHOR

Ken Winter is a follower of Jesus, an extremely blessed husband, and a proud father and grandfather – all by the grace of God. His journey with Jesus has led him to serve on the pastoral staffs of two local churches – one in West Palm Beach, Florida and the other in Richmond, Virginia – and as the vice president of mobilization of the IMB, an international missions organization.

Today, Ken continues in that journey as a full-time author, teacher and speaker. You can read his weekly blog posts at kenwinter.blog and listen to his weekly podcast at kenwinter.org/podcast.

~

And we proclaim Him, admonishing every man and teaching every man with all wisdom, that we may present every man complete in Christ. And for this purpose also I labor, striving according to His power, which mightily works within me.
(Colossians 1:28-29 NASB)

PLEASE JOIN MY READERS' GROUP

Please join my Readers' Group in order to receive updates and information about future releases, etc.

Also, i will send you a free copy of *The Journey Begins* e-book — the first book in the *Lessons Learned In The Wilderness* series. It is yours to keep or share with a friend or family member that you think might benefit from it.

It's completely free to sign up. i value your privacy and will not spam you. Also, you can unsubscribe at any time.

Go to kenwinter.org to subscribe.

Or scan this QR code using your camera on your smartphone:

❦

Made in the USA
Monee, IL
10 October 2022

15583001R00125